Stories from the Ballet

Stories from the Ballet

Cathay Books

Text and illustrations by

Ilona Borská — Milada Mikulová — *Coppelia*
Vladislav Stanovský — Ota Janeček — *The Sleeping Beauty*
Eduard Petiška — Dagmar Berková — *The Nutcracker*
Kamil Bednář — Ludmila Jiřincová — *Swan Lake*
Vladislav Stanovský — Luděk Maňásek — *The Firebird*
Olga Hejná — Jan Kudláček — *Petrushka*
Michaela Tvrdíková — Jiřina Klimentová — *Cinderella*

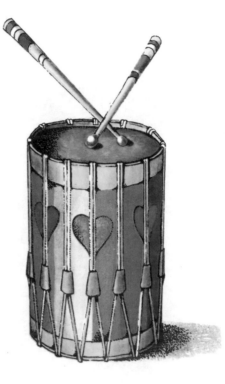

First published 1984 by
Cathay Books Limited
59 Grosvenor Street
London W1
Reprinted 1985

Translated by: J. M. Eislerová, V. Gissing, O. Kuthanová,
Š. Pellar, Y. Šebestáková, V. Vařecha
Graphic design by Aleš Krejča
This edition © Artia, Prague 1984

ISBN 0 86178 229 1
Printed in Czechoslovakia by Svoboda, Prague
1/20/06/51—02

Contents

INTRODUCTION

It was in the courts of Italy, following the Renaissance, that ballet first flourished. Catherine de Medici took the art of court entertainment with her to France when she married Henry II. It is from her great Ballet Comique de la Reyne *of 1581 that the birth of ballet is usually dated.*

In these entertainments, the courtiers and sometimes the monarchs took part. Court dress did not permit the ladies to move freely: their feet and legs could not be seen and they wore masks. Although Louis XIV set up a dancing academy, the Paris Opera, in 1669, it was many years before the ballet we now know developed. In the early 18th century professional ballerinas appeared, but they still looked like court ladies and were partnered by court gentlemen.

By the middle of the 18th century, ballet was still hampered by old traditions. Ballerinas still wore heavy dresses, and masks still hid their features. The stories were always about gods and goddesses and told by a mixture of mime, music and speech alongside the dancing.

In 1760 Jean-Georges Noverre published his ideas about how ballet should develop as a separate act, but he met with little success in Paris. He was able to put some of his ideas into practice while working in Stuttgart, but it was his pupils, in particular Jean Dauberval, who developed them fully. In Bordeaux,

6

Dauberval produced La Fille Mal Gardée, *the first version of a charming ballet concerned with ordinary people which is still fresh and lively today.*

In the early years of the 19th century the growth of the Romantic movement in literature, music and painting took place and from it came the Romantic Age of the ballet. The first Romantic ballet, an excerpt in the Meyerbeer opera Robert the Devil, *took place in 1831. The famous Romantic ballets* Ondine, La Sylphide *and* Giselle *were created in the next two decades, featuring supernatural beings and exotic locations.* Giselle *was the last great ballet of the age before this creative phase came to an end. Ballet in Paris fell into decline, but the next important stages in ballet history were already under way in Denmark and Russia.*

Auguste Bournonville was born in Copenhagen in 1805. He studied under the great Vestris and, in 1836, created his own version of La Sylphide. *The music, which contains hints of the original score, was written by Herman von Lovenskjold and is one of the first very important ballet scores. Bournonville produced a stream of ballets, such as* Napoli *and* Toreador, *in which he used colourful and lively national dances. This trend was also seen in the production of* Coppelia *in Paris, with its vigorous Mazurkas and Czardas.*

Marius Petipa had gone to Russia in 1847 and very quickly became ballet master of the Tsar's Imperial Ballet, a position he held for almost 60 years. During this period he produced over 60 ballets including the three great classics, The Sleeping Beauty, The Nutcracker *and* Swan Lake. *His collaboration with Tchaikovsky gave the world some of its most popular ballet music.*

Petipa devised such a rigid formula for his ballets that it was almost inevitable that young dancers would feel frustrated. There were already new ideas in the air, mostly coming from the group of ballet supporters led by Serge Diaghilev and Alexandre Benois and their artist friends. Diaghilev planned a season of Russian opera and ballet in Paris in 1909; Mikhail Fokine joined the group.

Fokine and dancers such as Tamara Karsavina had been inspired by Isadora Duncan, the controversial modern dancer, and this made them very keen to break away from the rigidity of the Imperial Theatres. The 1909 season was an outstanding success. The charm of Pavlova and Karsavina and the outstanding, almost animal-like, personality of Vaslav Nijinsky made such an impression that Diaghilev planned a season of ballet alone the following year. This was an even greater success and introduced the music of Igor Stravinsky to the West with the ballets The Firebird *and, in 1911,* Petrushka. *Nijinsky very soon began to create his own choreography, but being angular and based on two-dimensional Greek friezes it was in sharp contrast to the style of his dancing. Diaghilev enjoyed the scandals caused by Nijinsky's ballets, but when Nijinsky married the dancer was never welcomed back to the company. Diaghilev had already discovered the young Léonide Massine in a drama school in Moscow and encouraged him both as a dancer and a choreographer. Within a few years Massine was producing popular ballets such as* La Boutique Fantasque *and* Le Tricorne. *He, too, argued with Diaghilev and was succeeded by Nijinsky's sister Bronislava. She created ballets such as* Les Biches, *which still tell us much about the chic, smart atmosphere of the twenties.*

During this period Diaghilev discovered another young Russian choreographer and dancer, George Balanchine, who became ballet master of the Ballet Russe until Diaghilev's death in 1929. Balanchine created many ballets including The Prodigal Son, *with music by Prokofiev.*

It is not possible to tell the story of every ballet that has ever been performed in the pages of one book. We have chosen seven of the most famous — Coppelia, The Nutcracker, The Sleeping Beauty, Swan Lake, The Firebird, Petrushka *and* Cinderella. *Some of these may well be familiar to you, but we hope that we have captured some of the magic of ballet in their retelling, and that if you ever get a chance to see any of the ballets you will know the story that is being danced before your eyes on stage.*

Coppelia *is the ideal introduction to ballet for children. It is about a girl saving her fiancé from the clutches of a sinister doll-maker. It begins happily and ends happily and tells a story that is easy to follow on stage. Even the evil Doctor Coppelius is not treated too badly in the end. The music for the ballet was written by Léo Delibes and when it was first performed in Paris in 1870 the glorious combination of mazurkas, czardas and other national dances from eastern Europe made it an immediate success.*

The story was taken from one of Hoffmann's tales and was choreographed by Arthur Saint-Léon. In Hoffmann's version, the one told here, Swanilda sees Coppelius bring his doll to life by giving her the spirit of her fiancé, Franz. But in the ballet Swanilda tricks the Doctor and stops him from doing this by impersonating the doll, Coppelia, herself.

The American Opera Company first staged the ballet in the United States at the Metropolitan Opera House in New York in 1887, but Coppelia *was not performed in Britain until 1906 when Adeline Genée danced the role of Swanilda at the Empire Theatre in London. Strangely enough it was not restaged in London until 1933, when a different version based on choreography by Marius Petipa was staged by the young Sadler's Wells Ballet.*

The story is told in the ballet in two acts. The third act is a divertisement, *which the villagers stage to entertain the Burgomaster, and is not included in some productions.*

Coppelia

It was almost evening. The sun was setting over the town hall. The last rays lit up the gabled houses around the square.

Marie, the baker's daughter, and Anka, the potter's daughter, were sitting under a linden tree, dabbling their hands in the fountain. Shafts of sunlight glistened like goldfish in the pool. The girls tried to catch them, laughing happily as the cool water trickled through their fingers.

They were joined by Helena, the daughter of the weaver. She was as excited and happy as the other girls, for they shared a wonderful secret. They had been told the news by Teresa. She was the burgomaster's daughter, and knew everything that went on in the town. Tomorrow the news would be official, but for now it was the girls' secret.

'Shouldn't we tell Swanilda?' suggested Marie, looking towards the Rose Inn where Swanilda lived. 'She and Franz will be as pleased as Thomas and I are.'

Swanilda was usually sitting at her window at this time of the evening, making clothes for her trousseau. She was in love, and hoped to be married. But today her window was shut, and though the girls shouted and called, there was no sign of her. As the sun had now set and the square was beginning to get dark, the girls went home for supper.

The town square was usually a silent place at night. No sound came from the Rose Inn, the town hall, the church, the baker's, the china shop or the draper's. There was just one house — painted black, with heavy doors and barred windows — where peculiar things went on at night. Sometimes the noise sounded like thun-

der; or there was a loud hammering and the hiss of escaping steam. Other times, at midnight, there was mad, clanging music.

The townspeople kept as far away as they could. And from Coppelius, the sour old man who lived there.

But recently some of the young men of the town — Thomas, the miller's son; Karel, the carpenter's son; Jan, the teacher's son; and others — had begun to take an interest in the strange house. They strolled about in front of it, laughing and talking much too loudly, singing snatches of song and glancing towards the bay window, the only window that was not barred and was open from morning till night.

Sitting at that window was a silent girl, with a pale face and black, shining hair. Coppelius's daughter, some people said. Others thought she was his foster-daughter.

Nobody knew when she had come to the town. Coppelius had always lived there alone, and all of a sudden, one day, there she was.

Nobody saw her come or heard the noise of horses' hooves on the cobblestones, or the rumble of a carriage. There was no sign of a servant carrying in bags and boxes. One day, there she was, sitting at the bay window with a book in her lap. That was all they knew about her.

It was completely dark now, and the square was empty. The door handle at The Rose clicked quietly. The door opened and a fair head peered around it. Without a sound Swanilda ran across towards the black house. She had been told that Franz stood beneath the bay window more often than any of the other young men, and that the raven-haired beauty noticed him more than any of the others. Franz was the young man Swanilda loved and wanted to marry.

She was certain that the rumours couldn't be true, but she just wanted to make sure. She knew how much Franz cared for her. Only last

year, at Christmas time, Swanilda had been very ill and neither the local doctor nor the apothecary had the right medicine for her. Franz had harnessed the horses in the dead of night and ridden to the next town, plodding through a violent storm and deep snow.

Swanilda looked up at the dark house. Coppelia was there, seated at the window, a lock of hair black against the white of her neck, a book on her lap, just as usual. No one had ever seen her leave the house.

The girls, chattering around the fountain, had said she was lame. And as no one had ever heard her speak, she must be dumb. The young men had scoffed at them. They had all lost their heads over Coppelia, and talked about nobody else. Her mysterious beauty intrigued them, and, so it was said, intrigued Franz most of all.

Still, thought Swanilda, there must be some reason why she didn't come out and join the girls by the fountain, or sit and talk in the evening under the linden trees. Perhaps they were not good enough for her?

Swanilda was determined to get to the bottom of it. 'Miss Coppelia, can you hear me?' she called quietly.

The figure above remained motionless. Swanilda called louder. But still the girl did not move. Perhaps she could attract her attention by dancing? Everyone said that Swanilda danced better than any other girl in the town.

Swanilda danced until she was exhausted, and leaned against one of the trees in the square to rest. A sound came from the direction of the window.

'Good, I have made her look at last.'

But it wasn't the proud, black-haired beauty. It was old Coppelius himself, standing at the bay window, his small sharp eyes on the watch for intruders.

Swanilda clung to the tree in fright. The old man didn't notice her. He merely muttered something to himself and disappeared. And Coppelia, proud and mysterious, paid no attention. She sat motionless, her eyes on her book.

Just then Swanilda heard familiar footsteps from the other side of the square. Franz was walking towards the Rose, obviously on his way to see her. She stepped out of the shadows, ready to meet him. But to her surprise

Franz turned away from the Rose before reaching it, and crossed right over the square. Perhaps he had seen and recognized her?

But he was not looking at her. He was gazing up at the bay window. He seemed mesmerised, like a sleepwalker, as he gazed up at Coppelia.

So it was true, after all!

Franz was so absorbed, standing under the window, that he did not realize Swanilda was hiding only a few steps away. He stood beneath the window, bowing. 'Good evening, Miss Coppelia.'

That was all he said, but the way he said it! He sounded warm and passionate. He had never spoken to Swanilda like that.

From the window above came a little noise, and, believe it or not, the lovely Miss Coppelia noticed him. Her beautiful black head turned towards Franz with a slight nod, and she even waved her hand and greeted him. True, it was all done in silence, and in a reserved way. It was all over in a moment, then she turned back to her book. But still she had noticed him, the only boy in the town she considered worthy of a glance.

Franz stood there, unable to move, overwhelmed with happiness.

Swanilda, tears brimming in her eyes, felt utterly wretched.

In the window the huge figure of Coppelius overshadowed the girl. He leaned out, looking straight at Franz, a glint of laughter in his eyes. Franz pulled himself together and stammered a respectful greeting.

Obviously the old man had wanted to know whom his daughter was waving to. Perhaps he wanted to encourage Franz; perhaps he saw him as a future son-in-law ... Well, good luck, Franz. I won't stand in your way ...

Suppressing a sob, Swanilda rushed from the shadows like a frightened bird. Then, and only then did Franz see her.

'What are you doing here, Swanilda? Where are you going?' Then, as she turned away, 'Wait! What's happened?'

Swanilda's eyes were blinded with tears and she began to run away. The cold edge of the fountain brought her to a standstill and the tears ran down her cheeks and into the pool.

Franz came up to her somewhat awkwardly.

15

'Why are you crying? Have you hurt your-self?' he asked. 'Stop howling. Whatever has happened?'

Franz put his hand on her arm but Swanilda shook herself free.

She was dying to say something, to throw his betrayal in his face. But she could not utter a single word. She would have liked to remind him of so many things that meant so much. Had he not asked her mother and father for their consent to the marriage and bought her a real sapphire ring? ...

The ring? Swanilda tore it from her finger. The sapphire shone like a tear as it flashed into the water. Franz, amazed, stared after it, utterly bewildered.

'What are you doing, Swanilda?' he asked

her, still not understanding. 'I can never reach the bottom, it's too deep!'

'I never want to see it again, or you either!'

'Swanilda, wait. What on earth can have happened? Is it because I greeted Coppelia? I greet everyone in the town. That never bothered you before ... Surely, you under-stand ...'

But Swanilda was gone.

Early next day the people gathered in the square, for the burgomaster was going to make an announcement. A crowd of young people hurried out of the narrow lanes behind the townhall. Marie, Helena, Thomas, Jan, they were all there, laughing and talking. People pushed their windows open to hear, and others appeared at their doorways. Nobody wanted to miss the good news. The noise died down as the burgomaster appeared on the townhall steps.

'His Excellency the Count is coming to stay at the castle.' His words rippled across the crowd in the square.

'... With Her Highness the Countess.'

The burgomaster paused while the crowd shouted hurrah, as was the old custom.

'And for the first time we have the honour of welcoming His young Highness, too.'

The baby! Why, of course. He was born in the winter. They'd heard the news.

'To celebrate the birth of their firstborn, their Excellencies have decided to present the town with a bell made from the best bell-bronze, fashioned and decorated by master craftsmen in the finest possible manner. To-morrow morning there will be a Mass, and we shall bless the bell.'

'What is the baby to be called?' asked a voice from the crowd.

'Why, Jacob, of course,' cried the burgomaster. Shouts of approval and a burst of clapping drowned his voice.

Blessing the bell — that meant a public holi-day. And that meant no one had to go to work tomorrow. There would be dancing and singing, feasting and drinking from morning to night.

The burgomaster had something more to say. 'Servants are on their way, bringing twenty barrels of wine from the castle cellars. Twenty sheep are being brought from the pastures. Musicians are tuning up fiddles, and beautiful girls...'

'...are going to iron their dresses.' The voice was more like a shriek as the interrupter dashed off homewards. Everyone burst out laughing. Even Swanilda was smiling, smiling at everyone, smiling more than the rest of them put together.

She had moved away from the fountain a little while before to join the crowd, and knew that Franz was slowly trailing after her. But Swanilda was not interested, not in the least interested. Wriggling her way through the crowd, she got right up close to the burgomaster. There she stood, laughing gaily, showing Franz she didn't care. What a little fool she had been to let him see her cry!

All the bustle and commotion going on in the square drowned the loud noises starting up

in Coppelius's house, but the heavy curtains at the window could not hide the strange fiery glow in the room. So far no one in the square noticed it except an old woman at the back of the crowd, who crossed herself fearfully.

People were drifting off in groups, the old people talking and the young ones longing to dance.

But the burgomaster was holding up his hand again. There was one more important thing he wanted to tell them.

The Countess said her happiness would be complete if the new bell were to ring for the first time tomorrow as a wedding bell. And Her Highness would present a trousseau and a hundred ducats to any couple who got married tomorrow. The girls had been waiting eagerly for the announcement, for this was the secret that Teresa had already told them the day before. Her Highness was generous; long live Her Highness!

The burgomaster turned to Swanilda: 'What about you, Swanilda? It is quite some time since we drank to your engagement.'

Swanilda remained silent, her gaze fixed firmly on the ground, fighting her tears.

The burgomaster turned to Franz. 'Why go on waiting? A hundred ducats don't often drop out of the blue just like that...' The burgomaster's eyes sought those of Swanilda, and his voice grew more persuasive. 'Think of it: three chests of trousseau, sewn from fine white muslin and lawn!'

Swanilda shook her head stubbornly. 'I'd rather wait, Mr Burgomaster.'

'What on earth for, you silly girl? When will something like this happen again? A present like that, straight from heaven! Well, what do you say, am I not right?' He turned again, to Franz.

Franz shrugged his shoulders and the look on his face seemed to say: I can't understand the girl.

Swanilda's face turned red with exasperation. There he stood — as if he didn't know!

Swanilda caught hold of one of the ears of wheat fallen from a harvest cart and showed it to the burgomaster.

'Do you know the old saying, Mr Burgomaster? "At harvest time the wheat ears sense every secret".'

'Yes. When I was little I used to listen to the whispering wheat.' The burgomaster nodded and smiled. 'But ... that's just an old saying.'

Swanilda pressed the ear of wheat to her ear.

'The wheat tells me, Mr Burgomaster, that Franz has changed, that he has set his heart on another.'

'Swanilda, you are imagining it all,' protested Franz.

'Listen yourself, then.' She held out the wheat to him. Franz, reluctantly, put the wheat to his ear.

'No, I can't hear anything. Not a sound.' Franz shook his head.

The crowd edged closer round them, sniggering and laughing.

'You can't hear because you don't want to hear!' Swanilda stamped her foot angrily.

'You'd hear it all right, if you wanted to hear it,' she went on. 'Martin, you come and listen.' She beckoned to one of the boys from the crowd, and held out the wheat to him.

'It's true! I can hear it say something like that, something about a pale, black-haired beauty, mysterious and silent...' Martin pulled a funny face, nodding solemnly. The crowd laughed.

As the laughter grew louder Swanilda turned white and, refusing to join in, she broke the stalk and threw it to the ground. Then suddenly, to spite Franz, she began to dance with one of the boys.

Now castle servants in livery began to appear, bearing wine in token of tomorrow's festivities. The casks were opened and the people drank the health of their benefactors. Swanilda raised her glass high with the rest, and her laughter echoed through the square. Soon, all the young people were dancing.

As darkness fell and the fiddlers struck up for the last time, a harsh rasping sound broke into their gay tune, of a rusty lock, and a heavy door creaking on its hinges. Old Coppelius, wrapped tightly in his cloak, his face deep in an untidy tangle of hair and beard, hesitated for a moment on the threshold. He locked the heavy door carefully behind him, cast an angry glance at the crowd, and swept down the steps into the square.

Before he realized what was happening, the young people, glowing with wine and in high spirits, dragged him into their midst. As part of

the fun, one after the other, the girls invited him to dance ... 'Your favourite dance, sir?' ... 'A waltz, a mazurka, or, perhaps a minuet?' Poking fun, laughing and giggling, the girls jigged around the old man, bewildering him as he struggled angrily through the crowd. Wild with enjoyment, they danced in a ring closer and closer to him, ignoring his curses and threats.

He tore himself away from them with difficulty, nearly losing his coat in the effort, and vanished rapidly down a dark alley. Wherever could he be going so late at night?

Still, no one really cared, let him go to the devil! He was no sooner out of sight than they forgot him. They whirled around the square for the last time, then, tired and breathless, they broke up into groups and made their way home.

But Swanilda and her friends Teresa, Helena and Marie still lingered by the fountain. Something shining on the paving stone caught Swanilda's eye. It was a key — an enormous, heavy key! It must fit a very heavy door.

There was only one house in the square with a great door like that, and that was Coppelius's house. He must have dropped it as he pushed his way through the crowd.

The girls looked at each other in silence. The same idea struck them all, a daring idea, an intriguing one, an idea that made their flesh tingle ...

No one in the town had ever been inside the house. Apart from Coppelius, no living soul had ever crossed the threshold ... It was said there were wonderful and valuable things inside which Coppelius brought back years ago from his travels in faraway lands ... And here the girls stood, the key in their hands ...

But what if Coppelius came back? People said the house was guarded by a manservant, a real giant. Once, when Coppelius was out, someone had seen him on the steps ...

The girls were torn between curiosity and fear ...

The first step was already taken when they ran from the fountain to the mysterious house, Swanilda in the lead. She started it all.

It was not only the house she wanted to see. She wanted to see Coppelia, to meet her face to face.

The key turned in the lock. The door creaked horribly in the silence of the night. Surely, the whole town must have heard it!

The girls looked round in fear. But everything was absolutely quiet. They stepped inside.

Then they heard a sound outside. Peeping around the door, they could see someone creeping along close to the wall, a strange long shadow, almost too long for a human being, more like a monster ...

'How silly of you all!' exclaimed one of the girls. 'You are imagining things. It's a man, and he's carrying a long ladder.'

It was Franz. Franz, with a ladder under his arm, creeping under the linden trees as quietly as he could. The wine had helped him to summon enough courage: turned down by Swanilda, Franz had decided to run away with Coppelia.

He was sure the beautiful Coppelia loved him. Hadn't she returned his greetings, a courtesy she had never before granted to any of the other boys? After all, hadn't she even given him a sad little smile?

Well — if she hadn't *really* smiled it must be because she was afraid of the old man. Franz was not in the mood to believe anything else. He told himself that she had smiled at him and blown him a kiss — ever so lightly, raising two dainty fingers, no more than the fleeting touch of a butterfly on her lips, but there was no doubt about it ...

Coppelia loved him, Franz told himself, but the old man kept guard over her, watching her every move and holding her prisoner in her own home.

Franz had come to free her and carry her away. Hence the ladder. If he succeeded, they would marry in secret and set up their home somewhere far away.

Let Swanilda fret, let her fume. Let her cry into the fountain till it overflowed with her tears!

Having recognized Franz, the girls had drawn back quickly into the cold damp hallway of Coppelius's house. The door by which they had entered swung to behind them.

It was too late for them to turn back now.

Outside, Franz had his ladder propped up against the bay window, one foot on the bottom rung ...

Suddenly, he heard someone coming out of

the street on the other side of the square ... It was Coppelius, his head almost touching the ground in search of his key. He looked up ... 'Thieves, thieves, robbers!'

Franz disappeared like a flash, swallowed up by the shadows of the linden trees. Even so, the old man was able to catch a glimpse of him.

He laughed scornfully, muttering: 'Well, well; not a robber but a suitor ...'

And full of malicious joy, Coppelius vanished down the narrow lane again. Apparently he had forgotten about his key.

Holding their breath, step by step the girls moved farther into the house. The thick darkness now seemed a little less dark and they could see five tall wax candles flickering in sconces on the rising staircase wall.

Suddenly Teresa screamed piercingly, covering her eyes with one hand, and pointing with the other at the candles. Then Helena, Marie and Swanilda noticed that each candle was held by a human hand! A hand without a body, growing out of the wall.

'Quiet!' said Swanilda, her own throat taut with fright. 'Don't shout. They're only made of stone. They're sconces like any other, except that they're shaped like hands. What a horrible idea!'

The flickering candle flames sent shadows across the young girls' faces and across the faces of the statues on the balustrades. They seemed alive, and leering, as if they were whispering something spiteful to each other ...

At the top of the stairs a white door stood open.

Swanilda was the first to go in.

Right inside the door the giant figure of the dusky servant stood alert, a stick in his outstretched hand, the whites of his eyes gleaming in the dark. It was too late for Swanilda to turn back, she could not, her friends were crowding in from behind, clinging to her. She cringed, expecting a blow, but the giant was in no hurry. He held the stick high above her. Did he know she was unable to move — let alone run — that her legs were turned to stone? Or did he pity her, seeing the fear in her eyes?

Suddenly she understood it all. She was no longer afraid. The black servant was only a statue, all painted and dressed up, a kind of dummy.

Old Coppelius had some strange servants to wait on Miss Coppelia.

Very carefully the girls slipped past the giant figure. Teresa caught Swanilda by the arm.
'What is *that?*'

By the pale light of a flower-shaped lamp stood a Persian in flowing robes. He took no notice of the girls as he stooped over an ancient globe.

A dark-faced Moor sat cross-legged with his dulcimer. A tall Chinese towered above a drum. A thin piper was propped against a bookcase full of old books. Swords, guns and daggers decorated the walls and there was a weird and strange confusion of books on the floor, along with wires, screws, bits of material and tools.

An extraordinary room! All at once Swanilda felt sorry for Coppelia. How could that pale young girl live in a room like this? One would be terrified living with dummies instead of people.

Where was that lonely girl now? Was she reading still? Or was she asleep in another room? Imagine being able to sleep in the midst of all these creatures!

Here was her bay window. This was where she sat.

Swanilda swept the velvet curtains aside ... There she was!

Coppelia. Sitting bent over her book. Motionless, she read on and did not turn her head.

Swanilda edged back in fear.

Teresa managed to pull herself together first and said an awkward 'Good evening'.

The silence broken, the girls began to feel like intruders. However could they explain themselves to the girl?

But they were not asked to explain. Not even looking up, Coppelia went on staring at her book.

'How *can* she read? It's so dark,' whispered Marie.

'Fell asleep over her book, that's more like it,' suggested Helena, and her voice trembled. Teresa dared to touch the girl's arm very gently. 'She's as cold as ice ... She's dead!' she exclaimed.

Swanilda shook her head. 'She's not dead. Only she's not alive. She never was. She is a dummy like all the others.'

Swanilda managed to stay calm, though the discovery gave her a shock.

She was right. Coppelia wasn't real. She was a clockwork doll, a toy that needed to be wound up with a key. When Coppelius turned the key, the girl bowed and waved. But that, apparently, was all she could do.

So, thought Swanilda, this was my rival. This, Franz, is your precious beauty.

It was Swanilda's turn to laugh now. The joke was on Franz. She could laugh to her heart's content.

But instead, she felt a bit sorry for him.

The girls, released from the grip of fear, began to roam about the room. Their relief was so great that they burst into noisy gaiety.

'Oh, what a book! Just look at the size of it! And the weird writing, all squiggly. And pictures, more like ghouls and ghosts . . .'

'And how's our Chinaman today? Isn't it a bore, forever stuck with a drum? Look at his tiny pigtail, what a little goodie-goodie . . . Let's get them all going!' And with that Helena gave the Chinaman's plait a hard pull which started him drumming. Teresa's busy fingers set the Moor's dulcimer going, the cymbals clashing, while bang, bang, bang, went the Chinaman's drum. Only the piper was silent, still propped against the cupboard. Marie stuck out her tongue at him. Soon there was enough wild music and beating drums and sounds of gongs and bells to dance to.

In all the laughter, noise and movement nobody heard the door slam below or footsteps on the stairs. Nearer and nearer they came... All at once Coppelius stood in the doorway, like an apparition from another world.

'What's going on here? Who are you all? Scoundrels! You'll see.' Coppelius, in a violent rage, his arms flailing wildly, rushed into the room.

The three closest to the door, Teresa, Helena and Marie, slipped behind his back to the landing, and rushed away, so terrified they seemed to fly, hardly touching the stairs.

Swanilda, frightened out of her wits, stood cornered at the window, waiting for the worst. Now the old man would get hold of her. She hadn't got a chance.

Strangely, he did not turn her way but to his clockwork puppets, cursing as he switched them off.

Seizing this opportunity Swanilda slipped into the bay window and flattened herself against the wall.

The drum, dulcimer and cymbals were silent. All that could be heard was the old man, wheezing and muttering to himself as he hurried to and fro. Now he was moving towards the window. Swanilda could hardly breathe! He parted the curtains. She pressed herself flat against the wall wishing it would swallow her, hoping and praying...

Surely, surely, Coppelius must have seen her! But he turned to Coppelia as if unaware of the intruder.

'Darling, darling daughter! Are you all right? Nobody's hurt you?' He examined his dearest creation, mumbling and gently stroking her hair.

At last he seemed about to go. His bony white hand still clung to the dark curtains as he moved away. He stopped. He listened. Could he hear Swanilda's breathing?

No. He had heard something, or someone, beneath the window.

Swanilda could hear a faint sound, too. And the top of the ladder resting against the window shook visibly.

It could only mean one thing: someone was climbing up the ladder. Up and up, while Coppelius watched and waited.

Was it the girls? How could she warn them?

Then a familiar head appeared and the face she knew so well. It was Franz.

Lifting himself cautiously, he climbed

through the window, unaware that Coppelius was there.

Franz stood, peering uncertainly into the dark room. Then his eyes fell upon Coppelia, sitting by the table.

'I can't believe it! Is it really you, Miss Coppelia? And not asleep. Have you been waiting up for me? You knew I would come for you to take you from this prison and free you from your wretched jailer. We'll run away! Only come quickly before he comes back,' Franz whispered urgently.

He wondered why the girl did not answer. She must have fallen asleep. He reached out his hand to her. But an iron grip now clamped down on his shoulder, dragging him into the room.

'What are you doing here? What do you want?' Coppelius thundered. 'I know, you came to rob me! Admit it, you good-for-nothing.'

'No, I didn't want to steal anything, sir. I am not a thief. I wanted to ... I ...' stammered Franz, 'I — I wanted Miss Coppelia to ...'

'Since when does one climb through a window to declare one's love?' the old man shouted.

Then, abruptly, shaking off his anger, he let go his hold on Franz, and an ugly grin came over his face: 'Very well. Let's have a talk, then ... You'll see for yourself I am not as hard as people say ... A drink and a talk, that's what we shall have,' and he fetched wine and glasses from a cupboard.

'Now — what shall we drink to?' he said in a friendly way.

'To your daughter's beauty.' A bold toast, but Franz's voice betrayed his alarm.

They lifted their glasses and drank, but Coppelius spat his wine onto the floor when the young man was not looking.

Franz drank it all. The wine tasted strangely bitter, but nothing in the world would have made him admit it. Now, when Coppelius was in a good mood, almost smiling at him, he could hardly refuse to drink with him.

'So you wish to ask for the hand of my lovely daughter?' the old man began encouragingly, watching Franz closely.

The young man admitted this to be true. He looked towards Coppelia, to see if she would say anything. She was lost from view behind the curtains, but he thought he noticed peeping between the folds of the curtains a pair of eyes — blue, shining eyes. Yes, he was not mistaken, the eyes were watching him with sadness, fear and something like love ... But Franz did not realize it was really Swanilda he could see.

Coppelius shook him roughly, repeating for the second time. 'Have you any money to your name? Any property?'

'I have no property —' the young man admitted. 'But I have learned a good craft, sir.' Then quickly, 'I would be able to support her if you allow me to marry her ...'

'Penniless, but a heart full of longing!' Coppelius sneered, pouring more of that strange wine into Franz's glass. Franz drank again.

Poor Swanilda watched the scene from her hiding-place. She didn't know whether she was angry or sad. But stronger than anything was a feeling of glee and a certain triumph.

'Serves you right,' she thought. 'If you only knew what the thing you yearn for really *is!* Your loved one is nothing more than a collection of wires, buckram and screws.'

Yet Swanilda felt a strange, dreadful fear. What was Coppelius up to? All these questions and the wine — wasn't it just to make a fool of Franz? Or had Coppelius some other plans in his mind?

Swanilda managed to stifle her scream as she heard the splintering of glass and saw Franz fall back limp. Had Coppelius killed him? Was he dead?

The old man leaped up from his chair, his arms flung out in triumph. Then quietly, but ever so quickly, he went to the bookcase. He reached for his spectacles, and hurriedly turned over the pages of one volume after another, mumbling to himself very softly. Swanilda began to understand. Coppelius was being careful not to wake Franz, because he was not dead, but fast asleep.

Now the old man was searching feverishly through the books. Not that one ... not *that* one ... This one isn't it, either ... wherever is it? ... Finally it looked as if he had found the right one. He placed the heavy book on the table and triumphantly he moved towards the window where Swanilda was hiding.

Did this mean Coppelius was coming for

her? Had he known about her all the time? He drew back the curtain. Swanilda held her breath — but what was the use when her heart was beating like a hammer!

But the old man went straight to Coppelia.

'At last, at last, my darling, our time has come!' He spoke as if intoxicated with the thought of some long-awaited joy.

Slowly, carefully, he dragged Coppelia in her chair into the middle of the room, beside Franz. The girl sat as always — bent over her book.

Coppelius put on his spectacles again, leafed through the book on the table, searching for a certain page. His nervous fingers fumbled and shook. What was he looking for? What was he planning to do?

Now he laid one hand on Franz's forehead and the other on Coppelia's. His eyes shone with a mad glint. In a low, intense voice, he began chanting a magic formula:

'Let my arms be the bridge
His soul will cross
To enter my daughter,
To make thoughts buzz
To make her see,
Collecting knowledge
From the green crown of the wisdom tree.'

And indeed, Franz's cheeks began to pale beneath the old man's hand. All the blood was drawn away, while Coppelia flushed a delicate pink... As Swanilda watched, Coppelia's eyelids fluttered, her lips moved as her first breath trembled on them. She was like one awaking from years of sleep. She looked about her in wonder...

Franz sagged back in his chair, now without any sign of life.

Slowly, woodenly, like a clockwork doll, Coppelia stood up. Her book slipped to the floor. She stepped over and moved forward to explore.

And Coppelius? He was like one out of his mind. Like a bear dancing on his hind legs he jumped around her, shrieking in triumph.

Coppelia looked around the room, full of curiosity. Coppelius moved to embrace her, but she pushed him aside. She moved on and her face came to life.

She looked at everything. Everything was new to her. She touched the piper's nose, much as Marie had done before. Her movements were still jerky and unsure. Then she began to laugh and laugh.

'She is alive! It worked. I have achieved something no one in the world ever before achieved!' The old man's voice was more like a scream. In crazy joy he danced his bear dance again, clapping his hands.

Coppelia ignored him. She danced around the room, at first slowly, with careful, wooden movements, then more quickly, with grace and beauty. She was no longer a mechanical doll. She was alive!

She glanced at the old man as if she were seeing him for the first time. Her eyes moved over his features, guardedly, then with a gesture she invited him to dance. Coppelius eagerly agreed. He guided her through a waltz, correctly, a trifle quaintly, creaking slightly. Coppelia accidently tripped over the drummer, setting his clockwork mechanism in motion. The bold drumbeats drew Coppelia on and on, in wider and ever wider circles, dragging the old man behind her. His head began to reel, his breath came in gasps. He could hardly bear it. Spluttering, sobbing in pain, he pleaded with her to stop. But she twirled faster and faster.

Finally he managed to escape, falling half-dead into the chair. Coppelia burst into peals of laughter, clapping her dainty hands.

'I am thirsty.' Her voice was crystal clear. She picked up the bottle from which Franz's wine had been poured.

'Don't drink that!' shouted the old man, reaching for the bottle... Only then did he realize with amazement that Coppelia had spoken for the first time. What a lovely voice! How beautiful she was!

'I am thirsty!' the girl insisted. She stamped obstinately and held onto the bottle. Coppelius quickly brought a different bottle and poured some liquid into her glass. Meanwhile the girl had forgotten the wine, and discovered the book of magic. She turned the pages, full of curiosity, reading the strange words aloud.

'What does it say?' she asked the old man.

But Coppelius grabbed the book away from her, snapped it shut and thrust it into the bookcase.

'There is nothing there for a young girl. It is all secret symbols: memories of the dead, and midnight herbs, messages from the stars. You wouldn't understand it.'

By now Coppelia was no longer interested. The Persian was much more fun. She tugged his beard and spun his globe for him.

'What is this funny-looking ball?' she asked Coppelius.

'We live on that ball, my dear. And the finger of the universe spins us like this.'

'And who is this man?'

'A Persian star-gazer — an astronomer. I created him, too. One day I'll give him life just as I gave you life... Now I have a daughter; then I shall have a friend, too.'

'And that one?' she pointed to the Chinaman.

'A drummer. I made him to please you.'

'And this one?'

'He plays the dulcimer. He is here to play for you when you wish.'

'You made this one as well?'

'Of course. I made them all.'

'Even the one asleep there?'

Coppelia pointed to Franz. She touched his face. The old man pulled her back, irritated. 'You ask too many questions.'

'You shouldn't have made him. I don't like him,' said Coppelia with a toss of her head. She danced off around the room, holding up the hem of her skirt between her fingers. She came to a standstill in front of the giant who guarded the door.

Carefully, ever so carefully, she studied him, looming tall over her, holding the heavy stick high above his head. Suddenly, as if struck by a wild idea, she looked quickly around the room. Noticing the swords and daggers on the wall she seized a sword before Coppelius could stop her and with one bold sweep swung it over her head in perfect imitation of the dusky giant.

'Put it back at once! Do you hear?' Coppelius screamed, but in vain. The sword flashed high above her head. The old man tried to edge nearer to Coppelia to take the sword away from her, but he was afraid.

Swish, swish, the sword glittered in the candlelight. With one neat movement she sliced one of the candles in half and it fell to the floor, still burning. Coppelius bent down to put out the flames and as he straightened up again he found the girl towering over him. Petrified, he put out his hand to protect himself.

Coppelia, enjoying herself immensely, laughed at the frightened old man. She twirled and pirouetted, the sword waving in the air as she moved. At one blow off came the Moor's head. Beheaded, the puppet tottered grotesquely and the sawdust spilled over the floor.

'Don't destroy my creations,' begged Coppelius, clasping and unclasping his hands in desperation. He sprang to catch her but she simply took it as another game, and whirled out of his reach. Dodging all over the place she hid behind the cupboards and then jumped out at him, laughing all the time. She jumped over the scattered books on the floor, trod on them and knocked over the furniture in all directions. It was the sleeping figure of Franz which brought her to a standstill. There she stood, glowing, breathless, eyes shining, her black hair tumbling about her. Then she lifted her sword high and prepared to deliver a blow.

Swanilda screamed. Coppelia hesitated, disturbed. Her arms dropped gradually to her side. She cast a questioning glance towards Coppelius but he went on picking up his precious books to get them out of her way,

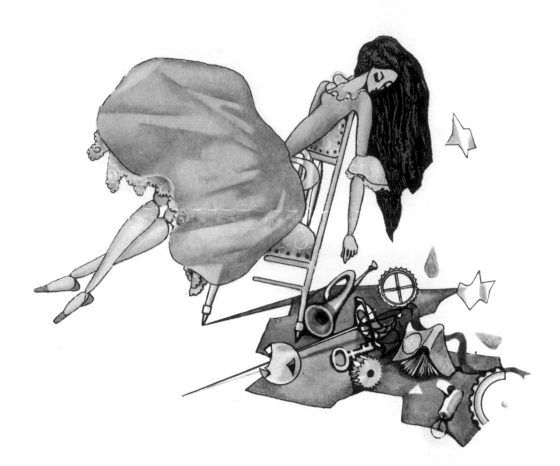

seeming quite unaware of Swanilda's scream.

But Swanilda's scream brought Franz to life. He stirred in his chair, stretched and rubbed his eyes. With an awful effort he woke up and slowly rose.

Coppelia did not notice him. She stood with her back to him, her eyes fixed on the old man. She seemed suddenly extremely tired. Her head dropped, her hands went limp, the sword clattered to the ground.

Coppelius quickly picked up the sword to prevent her from seizing it again, but this was unnecessary. Slowly feeling her way, step by step, Coppelia sought her chair. Coppelius helped her into it, gave her her book and pulled the chair hurriedly behind the curtain.

Franz stood up and looked about him. Where on earth was he? Why had he gone to sleep in this strange place? A weird, mad dream was running through his head — what was it? Now he remembered. And where was Swanilda? He had heard her scream, it was her voice. It was that which woke him.

'Go, go, get out of here!' Coppelius pushed him to the window. 'Go back where you came from. You are no good . . .'

Dazed, not understanding what had happened to him, Franz climbed through the window onto the ladder.

Now Coppelia began to move again. She sat in her chair, bowing and waving her hand, over and over again, her movements merely those of a mechanical doll. Livid and angry, Coppelius rushed to her and switched off her clockwork mechanism, and the puppet was still.

Swanilda seized this opportunity to attempt to escape. She slipped from behind the curtains and crept across the room, still trembling from the terrifying experience but happy because Franz had escaped safely. Happy to be free again, as she sped to the stairs she set all the clockwork puppets in motion. The cymbal player clashed his cymbals, the drummer drummed, and the huge guard in the doorway swung his fierce stick high in the air.

Now Swanilda was out of the room and gone.

The infernal noise which had started up drew Coppelius to the door but standing in his path stood the great giant violently banging his stick. Coppelius was helpless. He muttered and swore, then howled with rage. The staircase was empty and the door below closed with a bang.

Perhaps Coppelius tripped over something, or perhaps he was overcome with despair. He collapsed and lay, face down, unmoving, while his puppets ground out their blaring music and the huge man waved his stick as if it were a conductor's baton.

It was morning again. In front of the castle the menservants were laying long tables. Musicians were tuning their instruments in the summerhouse.

Groups of gaily dressed people had begun to gather in the square. The priest in his white surplice was waiting to bless the bell in front of the church. Everything was ready, scaffolding, pulleys and levers. The priest pronounced the benediction, and the great bell was hauled up into the tower amid cheers from all the townspeople.

Now it was time for the marriage ceremony. As the couples entered the church, the chattering ceased and a breathless silence fell: the brides were so beautiful, everyone felt the thrill of this moving moment. And the most beautiful girl of all, the last bride, was Swanilda. She walked with demure grace beside Franz, who gazed at her with love.

After the wedding the burgomaster pulled the bell rope and the fine bronze bell sent its first gay note ringing out over the countryside. It went on ringing until all the couples had come out among the cheering people.

Gradually the crowd dispersed and the people began to stroll through the shaded lanes leading to the castle. Beside the burgomaster walked Teresa and Martin, Helena and Jan, and, of course, Swanilda and Franz.

This group paused at one of the bends in the road to look at the view. The air was very clear and they could see the church spires in faraway villages, with blue mountains behind them.

'There is something special about looking into the distance. I wonder what it is.' The burgomaster was thinking aloud. The young people stood listening; it was an interesting question, for they all agreed about the charm of distance.

'I tell you what it is,' the burgomaster went on. 'It's the mystery of the unknown that draws

us. You stand up on the hill straining your eyes to see another, taller hill far away. The water you feel on your feet is just wet, the water you see in the distance is silver... The sun turns distant windows to gold... the distance contains mystery, and mystery evokes desire...

'Shall we sit and rest here? And I'll tell you a story, if you like, the story of one of my friends.'

The burgomaster looked round at the young people. He saw that Franz and Swanilda had also drawn near and were listening.

'He was about twenty then, this boy, and in love with a nice girl. He wanted to marry her. Everything was just as it should be.

'Then, one day, a strolling player arrived in the town. A shabby cart covered with tarpaulin, a painfully thin horse, a few stage props and two trained dogs — that was all he had. The dogs could count to ten, the man was a ventriloquist and he and his wife sang popular songs of years gone by.

'The best part of the show came at the end. In the darkened tent, by the light of three candles, sat a fortune-teller, her eyes tightly shrouded in a blue veil. The man announced with grandeur that he had snatched this priestess from her oracle in Thebes and in doing so nearly lost his life. Then he strolled up and down between the rough benches, borrowing personal belongings from the audience. Anything anyone had in his pocket would do, a comb, keys, a knife...

'Tell me, what am I holding in my hand? Tell me what it is?' he asked (of course wording his questions according to a prearranged code) and her answers were nearly always right, spoken in a dreamy, soft voice.

'It was simply a bit of fun and no one took it seriously. That is, no one except my friend. He was enchanted by this woman of beauty and mystery, a true sibyl, he felt. He went to see the performance night after night. If there were two performances he paid and stayed for them both. He was absolutely fascinated. For him nothing else held any interest. He was aware only of the blue veil, fluttering slightly, and the girl who wore it, as she gave her honeyed replies.

'He searched the dim outlines of her face behind the veil, longing to catch her eye. He could see that the narrow face was pale. A mass of lustrous fair hair fell down her back. But he could never see her eyes, they were always blindfolded. Yet, he knew from the voice that her eyes must be beautiful and sad.

'The gentle voice whispered in his ear, day after day, night after night. He could think of nothing else. He went on doing his work mechanically, blindly. After work he wandered the streets in a daze. Once or twice he dared to walk round the old cart. All he saw was the man mending the tarpaulin, and his haggard, worn-out wife sitting on the steps of the cart peeling potatoes with gnarled fingers.

'My friend was haunted by thoughts of the beautiful sibyl, imprisoned goodness-knows-where all day long. But he could never find out where she was kept.

'He counted the hours till the evening performance. He always sat in the same place, as near as he could get to the girl in the mysterious blue veil.

'Then one night he dreamed about her. She walked silently across his room towards him, her dark eyes shone. Now her blue scarf was loosened, and she held out her slim arms to him in a pleading gesture. Clearly she was begging him to save her.

'It was then my friend made up his mind to free her.

'His plan was to run away with her.

'He waited until night. Then he did not go to the performance, but hid behind the tent, waiting. As soon as the player started collecting coins, handkerchiefs and keys from the audience my friend crept into the tent. Before the lovely fortune-teller realized what was happening he caught her up in his arms and carried her out of the tent.

'At this point she started to scream and scratch him, with bony, bent fingers he had not seen before! Suddenly the scarf dropped, to reveal to my horrified friend a pair of dull, watery eyes. And then her wig fell off.

'Then people rushed from the tent, drawn by the noise in the street outside, and saw a furious, swearing woman, the actor's wife, trying to free herself from the young man's arms. What a scene! It was a show in itself. Everyone enjoyed the fun.

'How they laughed to see the sibyl's face

with its chalky make-up! A few incoherent words were all my friend could manage before he made his escape. The audience left, laughing hilariously. The unfortunate player pulled down his tent hastily. He knew he must move on to some place a long way away where the tale of his disgrace wouldn't follow him . . .

'That's the end of my friend's story. For some time he was the laughing stock of the town. His bride learned about it, too, but, being wise, she forgave him . . .'

'She must have understood the power of mystery, and the desire for the unknown . . .' murmured Swanilda, smiling at Franz.

The burgomaster beamed at them.

'Let us go now, shall we? We don't want to be late.'

The castle park was milling with people, all dressed in their best.

Sitting in their stately seats the Count and the Countess received the couples presented by the burgomaster. At the end of the long row Franz and Swanilda were walking together.

The Count's steward gave all the bride-grooms leather purses, each with one hundred ducats. Heavy wrought-iron chests crammed with linen for the brides were carried from the castle.

Suddenly the gaiety was interrupted by sounds of cursing somewhere in the crowd. Someone was forcing his way to the front, pushing aside anyone standing in his way — clashing even with the guards, ignoring their warnings and drawn swords.

It was Coppelius. He had come to state his complaints and demand his rights. Intruders had broken into his house during the night, he told them. There were three hundred of them, he said, if not more. They broke everything, turned everything upside down, tore his valuable books and damaged his instruments!

Swanilda was amazed. Did he really not know what had happened last night? Did he not remember his Coppelia and how wildly she had behaved? Had he forgotten?

It looked as if he had. Now he began sobbing, lamenting the destruction of what he himself had created in his sleepless nights.

No, he was not making it up. He stood there, pathetic and desperate. Swanilda felt sorry for him. She took her purse and ducats and offered it to Coppelius.

The Countess rose from her chair and drew Swanilda back. 'No, that is yours. He shall have his due . . .' She turned to her husband. He did not hide his irritation over this interruption of the festivities. But he took another purse from his steward and threw it to the old man.

Coppelius thanked him profusely, humbly. He grabbed the money bag greedily. The crowd opened up for him to leave, and shouts of 'Long live the Count!' filled the air.

The sun was setting once more over the town-hall. The square was completely deserted. Everyone was dancing up at the castle.

In the bay window of the dark house the pale black-haired girl sat bent over her book.

The Sleeping Beauty *was first performed in St Petersburg in 1890. It was based on* La Belle au Bois Dormant, *a fairy story by Charles Perrault, and the music was by Tchaikovsky. Many people thought that the music was too much like a symphony, but it has since become some of the most loved of all ballet music and* The Sleeping Beauty *has established itself as a favourite all over the world.*

The story is about a beautiful princess who falls asleep for one hundred years to be wakened by a kiss from a handsome prince. In the ballet the prince is shown a vision of the sleeping princess and led to her side by the Lilac Fairy. In the story here the prince makes his own way through the enchanted wood, after hearing the legend of the sleeping princess from an old woodsman.

In Britain, The Sleeping Beauty *is often thought of as the trademark of the Royal Ballet. It was chosen to reopen the Opera House in Covent Garden after the Second World War.*

With Margot Fonteyn as the Princess Aurora and Robert Helpmann as her prince, it was a spectacular triumph, one that they repeated three years later when they opened the Royal Ballet's first New York season.

The Sleeping Beauty *is in the repertoire of most of the world's classical ballet companies, including the London Festival Ballet which boasts a spectacular production by Rudolf Nureyev.*

The Sleeping Beauty

Once long ago, there lived a King and Queen whose dearest wish it was to have a child.

Every day the Queen would look out of the palace windows and sigh when she saw the townsfolk happily playing with their children.

The King was sad too and every day he would go hunting to ease his mind of his longing.

One day in a clearing in the forest, the King came across a white hart. He drew his bow in readiness to shoot but so beautiful was the animal that he had no heart to kill it. Instead, he returned his arrow to its sheath and rode on.

By-and-by, the King met a lovely lady dressed in lilac.

The King was used to seeing hogs and deer in the lonely woods and was quite surprised to come across such a fair lady.

'Good morning, King,' said the beautiful stranger. 'I am the Lilac Fairy and have come to thank you for sparing my white hart. For your compassion, I will grant you your most dearest wish. Before a year and a day is out a baby daughter will be born to you and the Queen. She will be lovely and sweet with no equal in creation.

'Ride home, now. The Queen misses you badly. Keep me in good memory and do not forget to invite me to the christening.'

The King was beside himself with joy and quite forgot the way back home. So he let his horse have its head and prayed he would get back to the palace quickly to tell the Queen the good news.

He rode on until he came upon six other graceful fairies who turned out to be the sisters of the Lilac Fairy. They, too, each greeted the King and asked to be invited to the christening party.

The King gladly gave them his promise and rode on.

It was almost evening when the King reached an eerie valley. There was nothing to be seen but bare uninviting rocks and a plain wooden hut.

Then, all at once, the wind howled menacingly and a black carriage drawn by rats and carrying an ugly, old fairy pulled up.

'Good evening, King,' she croaked on seeing him. 'I am Mistress of Evil and Ill Luck and if you fail to invite me to the christening party, your happiness will turn to sorrow. So, be sure to remember my words.'

The King hurriedly mounted his horse again, thankful that the wicked fairy had let him go. A moment later he found himself on the road leading to the palace.

A year and a day passed and sure enough the Queen gave birth to a beautiful baby daughter. The King and Queen were delighted and ordered a national holiday for celebrating.

The King summoned his Master of Ceremonies and the invitations to the christening party were prepared. The seven good fairies were to be the special guests of honour of the royal parents, and, because he wanted nothing to spoil the day of the christening, the King

put the wicked fairy to the back of his mind and did not send her an invitation.

The day of the christening party dawned sunny and bright and the palace was filled with happy guests. The beautiful baby Princess was there for everyone to admire and one by one each guest presented the royal couple with a gift for the Princess.

Soon it was the turn of the seven good fairies and as was the custom for fairies in those far-off days, the gifts they presented were very special magical gifts.

'You will sing as sweet as a linnet,' said the first fairy.

'You will dance as lightly as a feather in the breeze,' promised the second fairy.

'You will be beautiful and fair of face,' said the third fairy.

'You will always be gentle and kind,' said the fourth.

'You will be more graceful than a gazelle,' said the fifth fairy.

'You will make sweet music from any instrument,' promised the sixth fairy.

Just as the seventh fairy was about to kiss the Princess's cheek and bestow her gift, there came a mighty blast of wind and the door of the banqueting hall flew open.

The astonished guests looked in amazement at the ugly old fairy as she alighted from the carriage drawn by rats.

The Queen stood protectively in front of the cradle as the wicked fairy marched towards it mocking the guests as she went and wagging a wrinkled finger at the King.

'I have arrived, King, though uninvited. You have broken your promise but I am now here to keep mine.'

The King wrung his hands in anguish as the wicked fairy continued.

'I have come to turn the joy you feel at your daughter's birth into sorrow.'

The old crone bent over the cradle. 'You shall die!' she screamed. 'Die!'

A gasp of shock went up from the guests as the wicked fairy continued her grisly promise to the innocent child. 'When you are sixteen and have become a maiden of great beauty, you will prick your finger with a spindle from a spinning wheel and die!'

Then, with a wave of her magic wand, the old fairy disappeared.

There was a stunned silence and then the Lilac Fairy — the seventh and last of the good fairies — spoke.

'Be of good cheer, for I have yet to bestow my special gift on the young Princess.'

The Lilac Fairy looked down into the cradle as she spoke to the King. 'Although I have no power to lift the evil curse, the Princess will not die. Instead she will prick her finger and fall into a deep sleep that will last a hundred years. At the end of the hundred years, a King's son will awaken her with a kiss.'

The King and Queen were relieved by the good fairy's words but wanted to make sure that no harm could come to their precious Princess. So the very next day, the King decreed that all the spindles in the kingdom were to be burned and that no spinning should take place.

The years passed happily for the beautiful Princess but the closer it got to her sixteenth birthday, the more sorrowful the King and Queen became.

In the summer of the Princess's sixteenth year, the King and Queen decided to take their daughter into the country for a holiday. The countryside was particularly beautiful that year and they were all excited as they prepared to leave with a large entourage of servants.

The royal country castle was perched on top of a hill overlooking a vast woodland. When she alighted from her carriage the Princess clapped her hands with glee and set about exploring the castle.

She ran up a long winding stairway that came to an end in front of a large oak door. The Princess pushed the creaking door open and went inside. She was surprised to see an old lady sitting at a strange contraption with a wheel.

'Good day, old woman,' the Princess said. 'Pray, what are you doing?'

The old lady, who had never heard of the King's order about spinning wheels, answered honestly, 'Why, child, I am spinning. The sheep give me their wool and I spin it into a long thread to make warm blankets and covers.'

'Oh, do let me try,' begged the Princess wondering why she had never seen a spinning wheel before. 'It looks such fun.'

The old woman laughed at the eager child, not knowing that she was talking to a real princess.

'Of course you may try, child. It is quite easy.'

But no sooner had the Princess taken hold of the spindle than it pricked her finger and she fell to the floor.

The old woman looked at the still form of the girl lying there with her eyes tightly closed. Then, panic seizing her, she stumbled from the room screaming for help.

When the King and Queen saw their daughter in such a deep sleep, they were overcome with grief.

'There is nothing we can do to waken her,' said the Queen sadly remembering the curse of the wicked fairy.

So the King ordered that a bed of gold and silver be made up for the Princess right there in the castle.

'Go and fetch the Lilac Fairy,' the King commanded the royal messenger. 'She will tell us what to do next.'

The royal couple sat at the bedside gazing at the beautiful Princess. 'How lovely she looks,' sighed the Queen and they stayed at the bedside until the Lilac Fairy arrived.

The Lilac Fairy looked at the mournful couple. 'There is little I can do,' she said. 'The Princess must sleep for a hundred years. But I can make sure she is with people she knows and trusts when she wakes.'

And with that promise, the good fairy went around the castle and waved her magic wand at all the people working there. Whatever they were doing, as soon as the magic wand

touched them, they fell into a deep sleep.

How strange they all looked. The cook fell asleep tasting the soup. The groom fell asleep while brushing a horse's mane. The scullery maids fell asleep while they were polishing the silver and the groom's son fell asleep while he was scattering corn for the hens. In fact, even the hens fell asleep and so did the horses, and the dogs, and the cats, and the birds and simply everything that was part of the castle.

When the Lilac Fairy had finished her task she returned to the King and Queen. 'There is no more you can do here,' she said. 'Return to your palace and continue to rule your kingdom wisely.'

The King and Queen took a last look at their beautiful sleeping daughter and left the castle.

Standing outside the Lilac Fairy waved her magic wand once more and a thicket of brambles and bushes sprang up all around the castle making a protective wall so that all within could sleep undisturbed.

A hundred years passed. In that time the King and Queen died and another King ruled the land.

One day the son of the new King was riding in the woods close to the castle where the beautiful Princess still lay sleeping. He was very handsome and tall and strong, but he was a mite upset that a thick hedge of brambles had brought his retinue to a halt.

Nearby, a woodcutter was felling trees and the Prince addressed him, 'I beg you, sir, to rid my path of those brambles.'

The woodcutter looked up. 'I would dearly love to oblige, Majesty, but I'm afraid that thick hedge has magical protective powers. All my axe will do is bounce off those thorny branches.'

'And what is the secret it wants to keep so badly?' asked the handsome Prince.

'Some say that beyond is an enchanted castle and within is a beautiful Princess fast asleep. It is a story my own father has told many times.'

The Prince smiled gently. 'I do not believe in magic,' he said, 'but I am intrigued by your story. If there is a beautiful Princess beyond that wall of brambles, be sure I will find her.'

The Prince drew his sword in readiness to cut through the bushes, but before he could deliver the first blow, they parted of their own accord leaving a clear trail for the Prince to follow.

In astonishment, the Prince led his horse through the gap and followed a winding trail to the castle.

What a strange sight met his eyes. There were people everywhere — all fast asleep at their business and a trifle covered in dust.

'So the old woodcutter was right,' the Prince mused, 'but where is the beautiful Princess? I must find her.'

And with that he searched every room in the

castle until he came to the right one. She was there ... lying on a bed of gold and silver. The Prince moved closer and gasped when he saw the face of the Princess. She was the most beautiful girl he had ever seen.

So overcome with emotion was he that he bent and kissed her lips gently.

The Princess sighed and rubbed her eyes. When she opened them she was looking at the face of the handsome Prince and fell in love with him at first sight.

'You are here at last,' she said dreamily. 'I have waited a hundred years for you.'

As she spoke everyone else in the castle woke up and continued with their tasks as though nothing had happened.

The Prince took hold of the Princess's hand and let her escort him round the castle. By the end of the day he, too, was deeply in love and they decided to marry right away.

The chaplain was summoned to the royal chapel and he bustled in, the ancient dust from his robes flying everywhere.

But the Prince and Princess had eyes only for each other as they made their solemn vows.

So it was that the handsome Prince and the beautiful Princess were married. There was much rejoicing in the land which continued for thirty days and thirty nights. After that, the Prince and Princess lived happily ever after and became fair and wise monarchs.

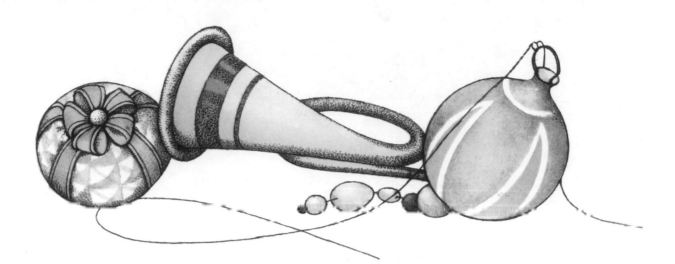

Tchaikovsky wrote his three famous ballet scores to order. He was required to write so much music to fit one scene and so much to fit another.

After the success of The Sleeping Beauty, *Petipa and Tchaikovsky collaborated on* The Nutcracker, *based on a tale by Alexandre Dumas, who was inspired by one of the stories of E.T.A. Hoffmann. Petipa fell ill and the ballet was finally choreographed by Lev Ivanov. The composer found that the story did not inspire him as much as* The Sleeping Beauty *had, but in the end he wrote a brilliant score. It was first performed in St Petersburg in December 1892, but was not a great success. Three years later the version we know today was performed and since then it has been danced by all the major classical ballet companies in the world.*

One of the most magical productions is performed by New York City Ballet and was staged by George Balanchine, who

was himself a student at the Imperial School in St Petersburg. When the Christmas tree begins to grow in his production, it carries on growing until it seems almost to fill the stage.

The story of The Nutcracker *concerns a little girl called Clara who is given a nutcracker doll as a Christmas present by Drosselmeier. That night, unable to sleep, Clara creeps downstairs. Drosselmeier appears and makes the Christmas tree grow and the doll come alive.*

Clara saves the Nutcracker from the Mouse King and as a reward he takes her on a magical journey through the Land of Snow to the Land of Sweets to meet the Sugar Plum Fairy.

The ballet was first performed in England at Sadler's Wells Theatre in London, in 1934, with Alicia Markova in the main role. In 1940 Markova danced the part again in its American première by the Ballet Russe.

The Nutcracker

It was Christmas Eve. In Frederick and Clara's home preparations had been going on all day. Delicious smells of baking wafted from the kitchen. In the drawing room their father was hanging glass ornaments and candles on the fir tree. Their mother was wrapping parcels and piling them up beneath the branches. The big house was full of friends and relations who had come to stay.

Frederick and Clara were locked out of the drawing room all day. They could hardly wait for the evening, when the presents would be given out. Frederick had tried to peep through the keyhole, but the key was in the way and he couldn't see a thing.

The big clock on the wall chimed the hour. The wooden owl sitting on top flapped its wings at every stroke. The clock had been made by the children's godfather, Uncle Drosselmeier. At last it was time!

Behind the door excitement mounted and the noise grew louder as more boys and girls — the children of their parents' guests — joined Clara and Frederick. As soon as Mother unlocked the door, Frederick, who always wanted to be first, hurtled in. Clara and the others followed on his heels. The grown-ups stood by the door, smiling at the excitement.

The tree, covered from top to bottom with flickering candles, glowed in magnificent splendour. Under the branches lay a huge pile of gifts of all shapes and sizes. One was for Clara, another for Frederick. Uncle Drosselmeier kept an eye on them to be sure the footmen didn't get them mixed up. The first one was for Clara. It was very big. Last Christmas she had been given a model castle with towers and turrets and dozens of windows. When you looked inside through the windows you could see tiny lords and ladies dancing and strolling beneath silver chandeliers to the tinkling tune of a music box. And standing by the castle gate was a tiny model of Uncle Drosselmeier himself.

Clara could hardly contain her excitement as the footmen removed the lid. To her surprise they took out a large head of cabbage. Then in the next instant it split in two and out jumped a big doll.

Frederick's box had a huge meat pie in it. It, too, suddenly burst open, and out leaped a soldier in a handsome red coat. Then Frederick's soldier bowed low to Clara's doll, and the two began to dance.

Everyone was amazed at how beautifully they danced. None of the guests had ever seen such toys before. Only Uncle Drosselmeier could invent such wonderful things.

But a sad fate lay in store for these lovely toys. The doll and soldier had barely finished their dance when the children's father said: 'Beautiful toys, really much too beautiful, Uncle Drosselmeier, much too beautiful for children. They might break them. Better put them away so that nothing can happen to them.' He ordered the footmen to take them away.

Clara and Frederick were not at all happy at having their new toys taken from them. What was the point in getting gifts that had to stay on the shelf? There was nothing worse than toys they weren't allowed to play with.

Their uncle felt sorry for them.

'Look,' he said, 'I still have something else here. Something that won't break easily. A present for the two of you.' He put his hand into his pocket and pulled out a wooden soldier in grenadier's uniform and riding boots. He looked rather funny because his head was much too big for his body. When his wooden coat-tails were lifted he opened his mouth wide, revealing two rows of gleaming white teeth.

'Who is that?' asked Clara in surprise.

'That, my dear Clara, is Nutcracker,' replied her uncle. 'He's called that because that's what he does — he cracks nuts, and very nicely too.'

Uncle Drosselmeier put a nut between Nutcracker's teeth, pressed down on his coat-tails and the nut split with a sharp crack.

Clara liked the little fellow in the grenadier's uniform, even if he did have a too-large head. If she could have put him in the room with her

dolls she would have done so right away. But he was not only hers, he belonged to Frederick too. She must let her brother have him for a while.

Frederick thought Nutcracker was a big joke. 'Some soldier!' he snorted. Frederick knew quite a lot about soldiers. In the glass-fronted corner cupboard he had a whole company of tin soldiers with cannons drawn by horses, and he was their commander.

'I wouldn't *think* of taking such a soldier into my company,' he said, 'but at least he'll be good for cracking nuts. Go on, crack them. Faster, faster,' he cried as he shoved nuts between Nutcracker's teeth one after the other as fast as he could. Finally he picked the largest one from the pile, put it in Nutcracker's mouth and pressed down on his coat-tails. *Cr-r-a-a-ck!*

However, this time it was not the nut but Nutcracker's teeth that had given way.

'Oh, you rotten thing!' cried Clara, the tears welling up in her eyes. 'You've broken his teeth.'

Frederick just laughed. 'He wouldn't have been any good as a soldier anyway,' he said, for he judged everything from a commander's point of view.

Clara, however, was not the commander of an army. Quickly she took her doll out of its little bed and lay Nutcracker down in it, tucking the blanket up under his chin. Then she took the white ribbon out of her hair and wrapped it around his head. Clara's mother always wrapped her head in this way when Clara had a toothache.

Suddenly she heard a sound of scurrying and

she thought she saw a small dark shape dart across the floor.

'A mouse!' she cried in alarm.

Frederick was scornful. 'Clara's afraid of mice,' he said to Uncle Drosselmeier.

'There's no need to be frightened, Clara,' her godfather told her kindly. 'Mice won't hurt you unless their king is with them.'

Clara guessed that her godfather had a story to tell about the Mouse King. She would ask him to tell it one day when there were no guests to interrupt them.

Soon the guests were saying goodnight and the candles on the tree were going out one by one.

'Clara! Frederick!' their father called. 'It's late. Time for bed.'

'What about Nutcracker?' asked Clara. 'Can I take him to bed with me?'

'Leave him here with the toys,' replied her father. 'He doesn't belong in the bedroom. You can play with him in the morning.'

Clara didn't want to leave Nutcracker, but it was no good arguing with her father. He waited for her to go to her bedroom, then put out the light and closed the door behind him.

Through the uncurtained window the moon shed a pool of light onto the floor. Outside the stars sparkled in a clear sky, and the houses were covered by a blanket of snow.

Everything was quiet. The whole house was asleep. Only Clara lay awake, thinking about Nutcracker. She kept tossing and turning from one side to the other until finally she slipped out of bed and softly tiptoed to the door of her room. She opened it slowly, then shut it behind her, taking care not to make a sound, and crept downstairs.

The clock was just chiming midnight. The drawing room was filled with silvery moonlight which penetrated to the farthest corner. Clara suddenly heard the sound of laughter and looked up. There on the clock, in place of the owl, sat Uncle Drosselmeier, his coat-tails waving and flapping like the wings of a raven with each stroke of the clock.

'What are you laughing at, Uncle?' asked Clara.

But he didn't answer and suddenly she felt frightened, and wondered whether she should run back to her warm, cosy bed.

Looking about, her gaze fell on the Christmas tree. To her surprise it seemed to be growing bigger and bigger. The bells hanging from the branches tinkled merrily, the paper windmills turned round and round, and the glass birds opened their bills wide and sang. The tree had suddenly turned into a dense green thicket filled with the sound of bells, bird song and music.

'Oh, how wonderful!' sighed Clara.

The china figures on the sideboard yawned and stretched their arms as if they were waking from a long sleep. The china blacksmith brandished his hammer. The flowergirl ar-

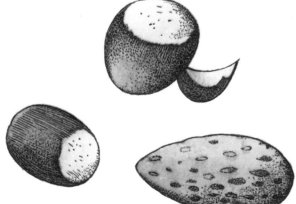

ranged the flowers in her basket. The musketeer drew his sword. Even the gingerbread figures, which had been lying forgotten on the edge of the sideboard, jumped up, slipped down to the floor, and started marching towards the tree, attracted by its chimes and music.

The toy cupboard was filled with bustling activity too. Behind the glass Frederick's tin soldiers were marching along the shelf just like real soldiers — left, right, left, right, left, right. The dolls, whose room was next to the soldiers' training field, were gazing out of the window, not paying the slightest attention to Nutcracker, who lay motionless in his bed.

'I wonder how he is, poor fellow,' thought Clara. But she couldn't seem to find the strength to go and see. She stood rooted to the spot as if bewitched, looking around her without moving.

The bottom shelf of the toy cupboard was where Teddybear slept. He had just got up and put his shoulder to the door. The door opened with a push and the sound of music drifted in; someone seemed to be playing the violin.

Clara noticed the open door and gave a startled cry. What if Nutcracker should fall out!

She was just about to go and shut the cupboard door when a strange sound made her pause. 'That isn't the sound of Christmas bells,' thought Clara, 'and it isn't the soldiers' trumpets either.'

It was a weird rustling, scraping and squeaking, soft at first but getting louder and louder all the time. Soon the noise even drowned the music of the Christmas tree. Small bright eyes gleamed from the cracks between the floorboards and beneath the skirting. Then sharp little teeth began to gnaw holes. The boards cracked and the plaster gave way as a horde of squeaking mice surged into the room. The gingerbread figures rushed towards the tree but the mice attacked them on the way and devoured them. Then the furry little creatures paused, twitched their noses, and looked around to see if there was anything else good to eat.

Clara couldn't take her eyes off the milling crowd of grey coats and long tails.

Then, as if in answer to a silent command, the mice lined up in rows like Frederick's tin soldiers and started marching in formation — one two, one two.

Clara could not help smiling.

But then, just beneath her feet, she heard a terrifying squeak that sent chills up her spine. The floorboards gave a sharp crack as huge sharp teeth bit into them from below. It must be an extremely big mouse that was trying to get into the room. It was. A mouse with seven heads pushed up through the pile of shavings around the hole in the floor. Clara quickly jumped up on the table. The mice were running about all over the floor — but the minute the large mouse with seven heads appeared among them they stood to attention and gave a smart salute.

The big mouse gave itself a shake, and as the dust settled Clara noticed that it was wearing a gold crown.

'This must be the Mouse King!' she exclaimed.

'Hurrah!' cried the army of mice and then they paraded in orderly ranks before their king and commander.

'I hope they won't hurt Nutcracker,' thought Clara, looking towards the shelf where he lay in his bed. A lot of noise was coming from the toy cupboard. Bears, donkeys, elephants and rabbits climbed out and lined up in neat rows. It was as if all the toys wanted to play soldiers, too. Then came the dragoons and artillery.

The army of mice gathered under the table on which Clara was perched. They made a horrible din with their squeaking.

The dolls were scurrying back and forth, packing their belongings into boxes and suitcases, as if they were thinking of running away.

Nutcracker's bed was empty. He had let himself down to the floor. The ribbon Clara had tied around his head was now a bright sash across his chest, and in his hand gleamed a small silver sword.

'Nutcracker!' Clara cried.

Nutcracker looked up and waved his sword as if telling her not to worry. Then he turned to the soldiers and she heard him say, 'Those mice must be driven out of Clara's house.' After that she heard no more because the squeaking under the table was getting louder and louder. The mice were evidently preparing to do battle.

Frederick's soldiers were ready too. The animals and puppets — the jester, knight, prince and night-watchman — all stood to at-

tention in front of the cupboard. Hurrying to join them were the musketeer and the blacksmith from the sideboard. And just in time. The mouse army had begun to move, advancing towards the cupboard, its lines spread out across the whole room — from the sideboard to the tree.

Nutcracker's trumpeters sounded the call to arms while the tin soldiers pointed their cannons at the on-coming mice.

Boom! Boom! The cannons roared, the mice squeaked, the drummer beside the cupboard beat a sharp *rat-a-tat-tat,* the trumpeters blew their trumpets, the donkeys began to bray, the blacksmith brandished his hammer, knocking the mice to right and left, and the soldiers fired their guns. The battle raged with the sound of blows, shouts, calls and the clash of arms, until Clara covered her ears and even — from time to time — shut her eyes. She was afraid to see what might happen to Nutcracker, who was in the midst of the combat, giving orders and brandishing his sword. And something very bad was about to happen!

The fiercest of the combatants was the Mouse King. All who crossed his path were crunched between his teeth, and Nutcracker's soldiers could do nothing about it. He advanced relentlessly, sweeping all before him, shouting brief orders in his piercing voice, until he found himself face to face with Nutcracker. He drew himself up, ready to spring, while Nutcracker, lunging with his sword, tried in vain to stab him.

Clara, terrified, cried out:

'Nutcracker! Nutcracker!'

Quickly she pulled the slipper off her foot and hurled it at the Mouse King. Suddenly the noise died away and Clara fell to the floor in a faint.

Everything was quiet again in the toy cupboard. A few scattered soldiers and the abandoned cannon on the rug were the only signs of the battle that had raged there shortly before. The dolls were seated in their room and the china blacksmith and musketeer were back in their places on the sideboard. But Nutcracker was nowhere to be seen. In his place stood a handsome young prince. He leaned over Clara, holding a scented handkerchief to her nose to bring her out of her faint. Slowly she opened her eyes.

'Who are you? Where's Nutcracker?' she asked.

'I am Nutcracker,' said the Prince. 'I don't know how to thank you for saving me from the Mouse King. You are the one who broke the spell that bound me.'

'The spell?' said Clara. 'What spell? Tell me about it!'

'It's a long, long story,' the Prince replied, 'but come, come with me to my kingdom. I'll show you things no one has ever seen before, and on the way I'll tell you.'

Clara put her hand in his and as they approached the tree all she said was: 'Please take a short road to your kingdom. You see, it's late already, and I must go to bed and get some sleep.'

The Prince gripped Clara's hand firmly and together they climbed the branches of the Christmas tree. Or rather, they weren't climbing but floating in the glossy green of the fir needles, among the glittering ornaments and sugar plums wrapped in silver foil, deeper and

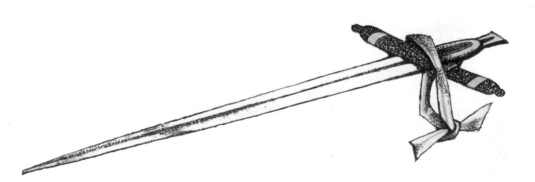

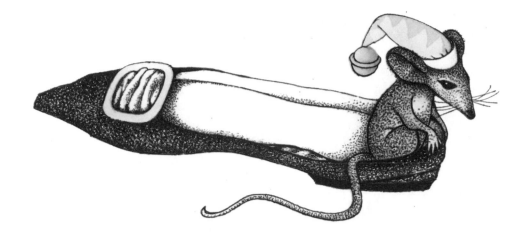

deeper between the branches into a green and silver twilight. Snowflakes drifted softly down about their heads, each bright as a star and breathing a delicate scent.

'Oh, how beautiful!' cried Clara.

'This is a Christmas-tree forest,' the Prince told her, pointing to the fir trees decked with fruit and silver chains — the bells in their topmost branches swaying in the soft breeze and filling the air with their music.

The snow fell softly and silently, blanketing all the trees. Dwarfs in bright-coloured caps scurried about carrying Christmas candles which lit up the way for Clara and the Prince.

Every now and then Clara thought she glimpsed a fairy-tale figure amongst the snowflakes — Puss-in-Boots, fairies dancing in a circle, Snow White fleeing to hide herself in the forest, Cinderella in her coach.

'I see fairy tales wherever I look!' she said to the Prince.

'A Christmas-tree forest is full of fairy tales,' he explained to her. 'No doubt, my story of the Princess Pirlipat is among them. If you like I will tell it to you. In fact, it is the story that I have promised you — my story.'

'Oh tell me, please!' begged Clara.

The Prince began. 'Many years ago, a daughter was born to the King and Queen of the land beyond the enchanted mountains. They called her Pirlipat, and she was the most beautiful of all the children born in that country.

'All would have gone well if the King had not had the idea of holding a feast and inviting all the knights of the land, as well as the neighbouring kings and princes. This was to be no ordinary feast, for the Queen herself made the soup in a golden pot, and all the plates, knives, forks and spoons were of silver. The very table on which the Queen prepared her special dish — spiced sausages stuffed with bacon — was made of gold and silver.

'These sausages were the King's favourite dish. And because she wanted to please him, the Queen took special pains, measuring out the ingredients with the greatest care and chopping and cutting whatever needed to be chopped or cut with her own two hands.

She was just cutting the bacon into tiny pieces when she heard a squeaky voice from under the kitchen table saying:

'Give me a piece of bacon, just a wee piece.'

'Of course I'll give you a piece,' said the Queen, for she was a generous person and this was a festive day when all the King's subjects should fare well, even the mice. (She had no idea that the mouse carrying off the piece of bacon was the Mouse Queen and that her sons were mouse princes.)

Hardly had they tasted the bacon when all the sons, nephews and nieces decided they wanted some more. They ran up her skirts and on to the table, eating up every bit. All that was left was one small piece and the poor Queen, though she tried her best, could not quite make it go round. She was left with one sausage without any bacon at all. That will have to be mine, she said to herself. I'll be sure to know which one to take.

The harassed Queen cooked the sausages, arranged them on a platter, then the chief royal steward carried them to the banquet hall. The noble company of kings, princes and

knights took up their knives and forks, their mouths watering in anticipation. But the instant the King put the first morsel in his mouth he turned deathly pale and cried out: 'Bacon! There isn't any bacon in my sausage!'

The Queen had to come out with the truth and told him what had happened in the kitchen when she was cutting the bacon.

'How dare they!' roared the King in anger. 'Mice! Mice daring to touch His Majesty's property! I'll show them! They won't get away with this!'

As is right and fitting in a ruler the King considered that anything that disturbed his comfort was a crime.

Luckily there lived at the castle the King's Court Inventor and Master Watchmaker, whose name was Drosselmeier — just like your uncle's. (Luckily for the King, that is, but not for the mice.) Drosselmeier the Watchmaker made several ingenious traps, baited them with the bacon the mice liked so much and waited.

The Mouse Queen warned her princes, nephews and nieces of the danger, but the smell of the bacon was too much for them. And so the Watchmaker caught all the mice in the castle; all, that is, except one — the Mouse Queen.

One day, when Pirlipat's mother, the Queen, was again cutting bacon to make sausages for the King she heard a loud squeak from under the table, just as before.

'You killed all my sons, nephews and nieces,' squeaked the Mouse Queen. 'Take care, for I shall have my revenge! Take good care of your daughter, Princess Pirlipat.'

The Queen was frightened out of her wits. She hurried to the King and they summoned the King's wise men. They decided that soldiers should stand guard outside Pirlipat's door day and night and that seven nursemaids should sit beside Pirlipat's cradle, each with a large cat in her lap. The King put great faith in the cats, for cats can smell mice anywhere and would surely pounce on the Mouse Queen the minute she came close to the nursery.

Everything was well planned. Nothing and no one could get to the Princess past all those guards, and yet the thing everybody feared did happen. How it happened no one knew. But one night all the cats fell asleep on the nursemaids' laps, and the nursemaids fell asleep and — strangest of all, for every one of them was

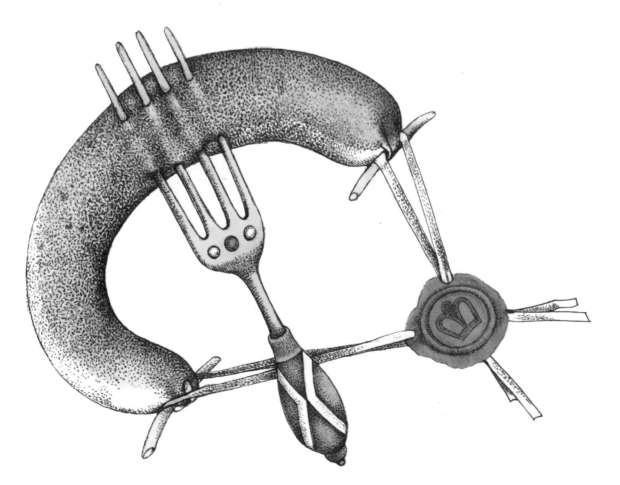

83

an experienced soldier — even the guards at the door fell asleep.

On the stroke of midnight, when everyone was asleep and all was quiet in the castle, one of the nursemaids suddenly woke up and saw a huge mouse standing beside Pirlipat's cradle. She screamed, but before she could gather her wits and before the other nursemaids had rubbed the sleep out of their eyes, the mouse had vanished in a dark corner of the room. The King's wise men found the crack through which the Mouse Queen had entered, but that was of no use to anyone, least of all to the poor little Princess, who from the instant the mouse touched her was completely transformed. Her body shrank and her head grew large and wooden, with a huge mouth — right there before everyone's horrified eyes. All that remained of the little Princess's former beauty was her pearly white teeth.

When the Queen saw what an ugly creature lay there instead of her beautiful little daughter, she wished herself dead. The King wept and wrung his hands in despair.

'Send for the Court Watchmaker!' he shouted. 'It's all his fault! If he had made really good mouse traps, he would have caught all of them — even the one that's hiding somewhere in this castle.'

When the guards brought Drosselmeier before the King he said to him: 'You have three days to find a cure that will restore Princess Pirlipat to her former beauty. If you do not have an answer by that time, we'll cut off your head!'

'That's bad,' said the Watchmaker to himself, 'that's very bad. Mending clocks is one thing, but mending people is something I've never done in my life.'

But the king's orders are the king's orders. And so he went into the nursery, sat down beside the cradle and gazed at Princess Pirlipat for a long time. So also did many famous doctors — all of whom finally shook their heads sadly and had nothing to say.

To make things worse, the poor Princess kept crying and screaming and nothing would calm her. The Watchmaker noticed what lovely teeth she had. 'With those teeth she could crack nuts,' he said to himself. And then out loud he said: 'Bring the Princess some nuts.'

The nursemaids brought a whole basketful of nuts, and the minute she saw them Pirlipat stopped crying, took one in her hand, cracked it between her teeth and ate the juicy kernel. And so she went on — cracking one nut after another until there weren't any left. When the last one was gone the crying and screaming began again. The nursemaids rushed to fill the empty basket, and Pirlipat cracked nuts from morning till night.

The Watchmaker sat and watched for a day and a night and yet another day, thinking and thinking. 'Can it be that there's some secret hidden in those nuts?' he wondered.

When there was only one more night left he got up and began looking in his books — heavy, old, learned books — and he pointed his telescope at the stars to see what they had to say about the Princess's fate. It was no easy task, for the Mouse Queen had made a really good, strong spell, taking pains to mix everything up so that it would last a long, long time. But the Watchmaker wouldn't give up until the books and stars had revealed their secret. When morning came, the guards took him before the King.

'Your Majesty,' he said, 'the Mouse Queen's spell will be broken if the Princess eats the sweet kernel of the rare and wonderful Krakatuk nut.'

'Splendid, splendid!' cried the King, dancing with joy and smiling for the first time since the tragedy.

'The only thing is,' continued the Watchmak-

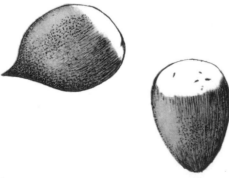

er, 'we have to find the nut first — which won't be easy — and then we have to crack it — and that's not easy either. The Krakatuk has the hardest shell of all nuts in the world. We must look for a young man who will crack the nut between his teeth in front of the Princess. And the rules of this magic are that it must be a young man who has never yet shaved, and he must give the nut to the Princess with his eyes shut. Then he must take seven steps backwards, and only then open his eyes.'

When the King heard what the Watchmaker had learned from the books and the stars he could hardly wait.

'Go,' he said, 'go and find the Krakatuk. And don't come back without it.'

Oh Clara, you have no idea what a difficult task it is to find the Krakatuk. It is such a rare nut that no one knows anything about it. It makes no difference where you start looking for it, in the east or in the west, it's never there!

The Court Watchmaker wandered over the whole world asking everyone he met, examining all the trees that grew nuts and searching in the market places where nuts were sold, but no one knew anything about the magic nut.

And so he went on and on until he finally came to China. One day as he was walking through a Chinese forest the poor, tired Watchmaker felt suddenly discouraged and seized with a great longing to see his homeland and he said to himself: 'No matter where I seek I get the same answer. Who knows if there is or ever was such a nut as the Krakatuk? Anyhow, if there is one, maybe someone has already cracked it open and eaten the kernel.'

And so the Watchmaker turned his back on the forests of China and set out on his return journey. He took good care to avoid all roads that led through the unhappy kingdom, for if someone were to recognize him and discover that he was coming back without the nut, that would be the end of him.

When, one dark night, he finally came to his home town, the first person he visited was his cousin, who made puppets and knew not only everything there was to know about woodcarving and painting but everything that went on in the town, too. The Watchmaker told him what had happened to him in the King's service, all about the sad fate of Princess Pirlipat and about the Mouse Queen. When he had finished telling about his travels in search of the Krakatuk his cousin burst out laughing.

'What a lucky thing you came to me,' he said to the Watchmaker, and with these words he took down a box from the shelf, opened the lid and showed him the nut that lay inside.

'Here is your nut,' he said. 'Here is Krakatuk.' And then he told how the nut came to be in his hands.

'Why, only last Christmas,' he said, 'two fellows selling nuts got into an argument in front of my shop. As they stood there shouting at each other, the nuts from one of the sacks spilled out and over the road just as a large wagon loaded with crates and barrels was going by. The weight of the heavy wheels crushed the nuts as if they were made of paper and when the wagon had passed all that was left of them was a pulpy mass. But in the midst of that pulpy mass I suddenly spied a nut — the only nut that had remained whole. Just fancy — the heavy wheels had rolled over it and it hadn't cracked! I thought it rather odd and I don't know why, but I bought that nut. I took it home and when I looked at it more closely guess what I found — the name Krakatuk clearly written on the shell in fancy letters.'

And that's how the Watchmaker found in his own home town the nut he had been seeking throughout the whole world.

Now he had the nut, but he still had to find someone who would crack it.

I wouldn't want you to think I was boasting, Clara, but at least three hundred boys tried to crack Krakatuk in front of the Princess, but all they did was to break their teeth. When the Watchmaker saw them fail, one after another, he finally sent for the son of his cousin the woodcarver. And, as you may have guessed, that was *me.* Everything was arranged. I was a goodlooking boy, and I felt sure I would be able to break the horrible spell for the Princess because no one in the whole street or in the whole town or in the whole country, for that matter, could match me for cracking nuts.

At the castle everyone had given up hope that someone who could crack Krakatuk would ever turn up when my uncle arrived with me.

'Your Majesty, this is my nephew,' he said, introducing me to the King. 'Let him try his luck. He's so wonderful at cracking nuts that everyone in our town calls him The Handsome Nutcracker.'

The King clapped his hands and the footmen brought in Krakatuk on a plate. I put it between my teeth, clamped down hard — and the shell cracked! I took out the kernel, shut my eyes and handed it to the Princess. All that remained to be done was to take seven steps backwards with my eyes shut. I was just about to take the last step when I heard the shrill squeak of a mouse behind me, and as I put my foot down I stepped on it, faltered and almost fell. At that instant my eyes flew open and I saw standing before me Princess Pirlipat, with lovely pink and white skin and golden hair — as beautiful as she had been before the Mouse Queen had cast her spell.

But this time it was I who was suddenly changed. I had opened my eyes before finishing the seventh step backward and so the spell was switched to me. My body shrank, my head swelled and my mouth grew big and wide. I had been turned into a nutcracker — a real nutcracker for cracking nuts.

Naturally, I did not stay at court. My face would only have reminded the lovely Princess and the King and Queen of the days of their great unhappiness.

I might have remained a nutcracker for the rest of my life if I hadn't found my way to your Christmas tree — and to you, Clara.

After this new tragedy my uncle, the Court Watchmaker, sat down to study his ancient books and the stars in the heavens until he found what he was looking for — how to break the Mouse Queen's spell.

'Nutcracker,' he said, 'the spell will be broken only if you slay the Mouse King who recently became the ruler when the Mouse Queen died. You must kill him in battle — and a young girl must help you do so. She mustn't mind your ugliness. She must help you because she loves you. If you find such a girl you will become your former self, and what is more, you will become the prince of a fairy-tale country.'

'And so it came about. It was *you*, Clara, who saved my life. If it hadn't been for you I would have remained a wooden nutcracker until my jaws finally broke and I was thrown out onto the dust heap.'

Clara blushed at these words of praise and was

very relieved when she thought of how he *might* have ended. But out loud she said: 'Oh what a lovely smell! What is it that smells so nice?'

'That's the smell of Orange Brook,' answered Prince Nutcracker.

Clara had been so fascinated by his story that she had forgotten to look about her. They had left Christmas-tree forest far behind and were walking together over a lush, emerald green meadow, their feet barely touching the ground. Alongside them burbled Orange Brook, filling the air with its scent of fresh orange juice. Slices of orange bobbed on the ripples, looking just like small goldfish.

'Oh how lovely,' cried Clara, 'how perfectly lovely!'

Soft music played as they drifted down the emerald meadow, each blade of grass sounding its delicate note as their feet touched it.

The Prince took her hand. 'Give a push with your foot, Clara, a good push.' And with that they both rose high above the meadow and floated through the warm blue air above the brook.

'We're flying! Oh, Prince Nutcracker, we're flying!' cried Clara in amazement.

'Yes. We're flying to make the journey shorter,' he said. Then he pointed downward. 'Look, that's Lemon River down there below us. We still have to cross that before we reach our destination.'

The yellow glare from the river made Clara blink. Soon the air was filled with the scent of lemons, which reminded Clara of her mother, for that was the smell that filled the whole house before the holidays when she was grating lemon rind for the Christmas cakes and pies.

'Shall we be there soon?' asked Clara. 'I shouldn't like mother to be worried about me.'

'Yes, in just a little while,' the Prince replied. 'We'll take a boat across Rose Lake right to the city gates. We could fly over the lake, but I'm afraid you might get dizzy. The smell of the waves in Rose Lake is even stronger than that of Orange Brook or Lemon River.'

With that Clara and the Prince alighted on the shores of the lake, which smelled like a rose garden. There just before them was a large shell, drawn by two golden dolphins. The shell was as big as a boat and was decked with precious gems whose bright flashing hues were reflected in the waves.

Out of the shell leaped six little boys, no bigger than the chocolate boys on the Christmas tree. They spread out a large carpet covered with golden coins — but before Clara could ask if the coins were filled with chocolate off they went, flying over the waves. The dolphins sped along so fast that the water on either side of the boat was churned into foam.

The little boys sang and danced until they set the shell rocking.

Clara laughed and laughed. 'What fun, it's just like being in a swing.' She was surprised that she wasn't afraid. Suddenly, as Clara gazed into the water, she glimpsed a lovely girl's face, as if it were reflected in a hundred mirrors.

'Pirlipat, Pirlipat,' she cried.

'No, that isn't Pirlipat,' said the Prince, 'that's *you*, Clara.'

Once again Clara blushed a deep pink. She was flattered and glad that she looked like a princess, but she did not understand how it could have happened.

Suddenly the city gates towered before them.

'Look, the guards are already waiting,' said the Prince.

Clara didn't know where to look first. Spreading out before her was a city with sugar towers and turrets, streets paved with candies, and gingerbread gates. In front of the gates in the shade of chocolate trees, whose branches were laden with jellies and sweetmeats, stood the silver soldiers of the municipal guard. As Clara and the Prince stepped out they gave a smart salute and the little boat boys played a fanfare on small drums and trumpets. As if at a given signal all the sugar, gingerbread and candy windows in the town flew open and out of every one leaned a doll. Some were wearing

paper gowns and others were dressed in brightest silver foil. All of them clapped their hands and cried out:

'Long live Prince Nutcracker! Hurrah! Hurrah! Hurrah!'

Clara and the Prince were greeted at the gates by a noble lord dressed in a handsomely embroidered coat. He led them to the beautiful sugar castle. The people waved and shouted as they passed and the streets were filled with music and dancing.

The noble lord walked in front, making way for them between the dolls and snowmen.

'Oh-oh-oh!' breathed Clara when they came to the steps of the sugar castle.

It was a very big castle, much bigger than the one Uncle Drosselmeier had given her and Frederick last Christmas. His was a doll's castle, but this one was big enough for Clara to go into.

The castle glowed brightly. The roof and turrets sparkled as if covered with the stars of all the Christmas trees in the world. The noble lord struck the ground three times with his gold-tipped cane and the gates of the castle opened. Out marched twelve pageboys, each bearing a large bouquet of flowers. They stood in two rows, casting blossoms on the path to make a soft, fragrant carpet for Clara and Prince Nutcracker to walk on as they went into the castle.

'What a pity to trample such beautiful flowers,' Clara said.

'You needn't feel so sad,' said the Prince, 'look behind you.'

Clara turned and stood still in astonishment, for the flowers they had walked over were standing upright again. And growing in their footsteps were roses, carnations, daisies and bluebells which swayed gently in the breeze,

beckoning Clara to come and pick them.

After the pages danced four beautiful Princesses, who greeted Prince Nutcracker with tears and embraces and shouts of joy.

'Our brother, our dear, dear brother.'

When the Prince finally managed to free himself, he took Clara by the hand and said to them, 'My beloved sisters, this is Clara. It was she who saved my life when I fought the Mouse King.'

The Princesses rushed to embrace her, and showered her with thanks. Such a display of emotion made Clara feel shy and she was quite glad when they led her inside the castle where a feast had been laid out for them in the banquet hall.

Prince Nutcracker sat at the head of the table and told all about his many adventures, while the pages served Clara's favourite dishes. There were nut rolls, nut bars and marzipan sweets on large crystal platters which glittered as if carved from ice. And there was everything to drink — orange juice, lemon juice and raspberry juice served in tall, crystal goblets —

and many more delicious things. Then the Princesses cut her a slice from a huge cake decorated with a picture in sugar and chocolate icing of Nutcracker's battle with the Mouse King and topped with a large, big candy slipper just like the one that belonged to Clara. Then there was cocoa, chocolate or tea to drink with the cake.

At the height of the festivities Prince Nutcracker stood up and said: 'Dear Clara, if you would like to come and live with us here in this castle, it would make me and my sisters very happy.'

'I should love to stay,' replied Clara, 'but I must go home first — to get some sleep, and tell my mother all about everything. After that I'll come back.'

When Clara woke on Christmas Day morning the adventures of the previous night seemed far away. But she vowed that, one day, she really would return to the fairy-tale land where Prince Nutcracker rules with his bride, Princess Pirlipat.

The story of Swan Lake *is perhaps the best-known of all in ballet. But what is not so well-known is that when the ballet was first produced in Moscow in 1877 it was not a success, despite the beauty of Tchaikovsky's score.* Swan Lake *was restaged in 1895 as a memorial to Tchaikovsky with the music rearranged and with different choreography. Since then it has become one of the most staged ballets of all time.*

The ballet has four acts, the second and fourth of which are often called the 'White' acts, because of the white costumes the dancers wear. They were choreographed by Ivanov for the 1895 production, the elaborate court scenes of the first and third acts being choreographed by Marius Petipa, the ballet master of the Imperial Ballet.

The story told here and some versions used for the ballet differ slightly. In many ballets, the heroine, Odette, and the prince, Siegfried, throw themselves into the lake and are reunited in death. Here, we tell the longer, German version often used in Russian productions of the ballet in which Siegfried fights the wicked Baron von Rotenbart (Redbeard) and kills him. Odette is freed from his power and the lovers are happily reunited.

Swan Lake *was first performed in the United States in 1911 at the Metropolitan Opera House with Catherine Geltser and Mikhail Mordkin in the leading roles. In Great Britain, it was not performed until 1934, when Alicia Markova and Robert Helpmann danced the leading roles at Sadler's Wells Theatre in London.*

Swan Lake

Once upon a time, in a faraway kingdom, there lived a widowed Queen who had one son. On the eve of his twenty-first birthday she said to him: 'You are old enough now, my son, to choose a bride — one worthy to take her place beside you when you become king.'

But the Prince was not interested in getting married. He turned away and looked out of the window, watching the trees swaying in the wind.

'Mother,' he said, 'I do not wish to have a wife — not yet. I am as happy as I am. Please do not talk about it.'

'But you are a Prince, Siegfried,' his mother replied, 'and the sooner you make your choice, the better for everyone.'

The Prince sighed. 'Well, what must I do, Mother?' he asked.

'Leave it to me. I will arrange everything,' said the Queen. 'I shall hold a ball and invite the most beautiful girls from all the noble families. You must choose a bride from them.'

Prince Siegfried sighed again. 'All right, if that is what you want. But, please — not yet. All I want to do is hunt. I love the long days in the woods with my companions. Let me enjoy it some more before I have to think about getting married.'

'You can hunt all day tomorrow,' said his mother, 'but the day after that you must choose your bride at the ball.'

'I am happy for you to choose her yourself, Mother,' said the Prince, glad that the discussion was at an end. 'I am only interested in being out-of-doors with the hunt.'

The Queen looked at her handsome son and thought to herself that once he saw the lovely girls he would soon realize that there were other things to live for besides hunting. But aloud she simply said: 'Go and enjoy your sport. You are young and free. You need not trouble your head about the ball. I shall make all the preparations.'

The next day the young Prince rode out early through the castle gates and set off toward the distant forest with his friend and constant companion, Jan, and several other hunters.

They rode for the whole day, but somehow, this time, hunting did not amuse the Prince as it usually did. He rode about the countryside at random, but could not shake off a feeling of uneasiness. He didn't seem to care or notice which way he went. As evening fell and the hunting party turned wearily toward home, they found themselves near the Stone Forest. Frightening tales were told about this forest, so that few people dared to go in among the thick trees.

As they moved into the shadow of the trees skirting the wood, they seemed to be in a different world. The utter stillness oppressed them. Not a twig stirred. There was no sound of bird song. Even the horses felt the oppressive atmosphere.

'Look, Jan,' shouted the Prince suddenly, pointing upward at the darkening sky.

'Swans flying. What's strange about that?' said Jan.

'But don't you see the leading swan?' cried the Prince. 'Are you blind? It is wearing a golden crown!'

'So it is,' murmured Jan.

They watched the flock winging swiftly across the sky.

'It must be the Queen of the Swans,' cried the Prince. 'We are not likely to see the Swan Queen more than once in a lifetime. Some people *never* see her.'

He raised his bow, then lowered it, and did not shoot at the swan. He felt a strange longing. The flock flew over their heads and landed somewhere deep in the mysterious forest.

Again all was still and silent.

The men sprang from their horses and ran into the wood. It was very eerie and dark. The tall oak trees blocked out the sunlight and the moss made a thick carpet that absorbed all

sound. They thrust their way in through the undergrowth between the towering trees and were soon lost.

It seemed hopeless to try to follow the swans, but nothing would stop the Prince, so the other men pressed on with him.

Suddenly Jan called and pointed to some water gleaming through the trees. They came out on the shores of a lake, and there was the flock of beautiful white swans, led by the swan with the golden crown.

The Prince raised his bow and took aim, but then lowered it again.

'I cannot shoot.' He caught his breath '— it

would be like killing a human being. Jan, it isn't a swan, it's a beautiful girl, it's the princess I'm seeking. The swan shall be mine. I shall win her for my bride!'

'Are you mad, Prince?' said Jan. 'One moment you are keen to hunt, then, suddenly you put down your bow and talk as if you were bewitched. But people say that the Stone Forest is full of magic. They say a powerful enchanter rules here.'

'The Swan Queen has bewitched me,' whispered the Prince. 'Look, Jan, how graceful she is! How delicate! Look, they're going to take wing. They'll fly away and leave us!'

The surface of the lake was rapidly becoming indistinct in the gathering dusk. In the centre the swans were spreading their wings and stretching their necks, ready to rise from the water. The darker it grew, the whiter they seemed to be. On the head of the one in front the golden crown sparkled in the last fading rays of the setting sun.

The Swan Queen rose in the air and flew straight towards them.

'She's flying this way, Jan,' the Prince shouted. 'She has noticed me. I am sure she has.'

But just before she reached them, the Swan Queen changed direction, circled around and rose high above the lake. Her companions kept behind her, as though drawn along with her by an invisible thread.

'After her — I mustn't lose sight of her,' shouted the Prince.

Jan caught his arm and tried to hold him back. But the Prince shook him off, and before the others knew what had happened, he had disappeared from sight into the shadows of the forest.

They set off after him, stumbling over roots and stones. Jan turned to his companions. 'Come,' he urged them. 'We must find him!'

'Let's keep following,' said an old experienced archer. 'We shall catch up with him sooner or later, for the forest must end somewhere.'

'I'm afraid he may be out of his mind,' said Jan. 'I've never seen him act so strangely before.'

'You think he has fallen in love with a swan?' said the old archer, with a laugh. 'Whoever heard of such a thing! A swan is beautiful, but it looks at you with cold eyes, and you cannot love a creature who is never happy except in cold water!'

'That's presuming it really *is* a swan,' said Jan.

The moonlight lit up the path clearly. The men thrust through the bushes in the direction they thought the Prince had taken.

He continued in the line of the swans' flight. The undergrowth was less thick and tangled now. He was able to run faster between the great round trunks of the oaks.

Then there was an opening among the trees and the Prince found himself in a broad clearing. In the pale moonlight he could see the blackened stones of a ruined castle which must have been burned down many years ago. Its jagged tower stood out like a petrified hand against the sky.

The Prince was out of breath and sat down wearily on a rock to rest. How shall I ever find her in this wilderness? I haven't any idea where she can be, he thought.

He looked up at the moon, feeling baffled, but the moon seemed very far away and still and cold — like everything in this Stone Forest.

Then through the trees he saw another glow of white. It was an ethereal creature in human form — the form of a lovely, fair-skinned girl with golden hair flowing down over her shoulders and eyes as blue as the sky at noon. She wore a white dress which trailed on the grass, her feet were bare and her legs were straight and slender as she walked slowly towards him.

He drew in his breath sharply. Could such beauty be real?

The Prince spoke to her and was surprised that she answered him — and even more amazed that she seemed to know him.

'Prince Siegfried,' she said. 'I remember you so well. You are tall now, but you have not changed.'

'Who are you?' he whispered in awe.

'I am the daughter of one of your father's counsellors who died,' she told him. 'The lord of this forest turned me into a swan in revenge for not getting his own way, and all the girls of my train with me.'

'So the Stone Forest *does* have a master. The tales they tell are true?'

'Yes. He is called Redbeard,' she said. 'He is very wicked and cruel.'

The enchanter might prove to be a formidable enemy but just at this moment the Prince did not worry about him. He was too delighted at finding that the swan he had fallen in love with was really this lovely girl.

'So you were a swan only when you were under a spell,' said the Prince. 'But how is it that now I can see you in your true form? What broke the spell?'

'Each night we are allowed to resume our human shape for a while. But then we are twice as unhappy later, when the white spell seizes us again. Suddenly our hands stiffen and grow feathers, our necks stretch out, and we turn into swans. The forest spirits mock me as my crown of golden hair becomes a real crown of gold. Redbeard laughs maliciously at us. Wait till the autumn, when the leaves shrivel on the oaks, and you will hear his sharp, hissing laughter. It is worse than the frost and the fierce storms.'

The Prince was deeply moved. He took her hands in his.

'How can I help you?' he asked. 'Tell me what I must do. I long to save you. I have never felt so drawn to anyone as to you.'

'And I am drawn to you, Prince,' replied the enchanted girl. 'When you aimed your arrow at me, it was as though your hand had touched me. When you looked up at me by the shores of the lake, it was as though you had caressed me with your hand. I have never flown as slowly as that before. Then I saw you running and allowed you to find me. No one has ever seen us after sunset when we change from swans to our human shape.'

'I had to follow you. Even as a swan you enchanted me. But now that I see you as you really are,' he went on, 'I know that you are the loveliest girl in all the world. What is your name?'

'I am Odette.'

'Odette, my Odette,' the Prince said slowly. 'Now you need fear no more. I am here with you. I shall protect you and never leave you!'

'I am afraid your promises are in vain,' said Odette sadly. 'In a short while we shall be changed into swans again, and you have no wings to fly with us.'

'But I shall release you from the spell, Odette.'

She shook her head and tears were in her eyes.

'You are powerless against such magic, my Prince.'

'Is it not within human power to overcome the dark forces of evil?'

'Yes, Prince, it is, but you would have to ...' Odette hesitated.

'What would I have to do? I'll do anything,' the Prince promised eagerly. 'Only tell me.'

'You would have to give me the most precious thing a human being has: you would have to give me... your love,' whispered Odette, and she bowed her head.

'But I *do* give you my love, Odette,' said the Prince, pressing her hand and looking at her with shining eyes. 'I loved you the moment I first saw you.'

Odette smiled sadly. 'The time will come soon — perhaps even tomorrow, Prince — when you will see other beautiful girls — rich, noble girls — and you will forget the sad girl in the forest.'

'I want nobody else but you, Odette,' cried the Prince. 'I shall save you with my love.' And he was about to take her in his arms, but at that moment Odette was transformed before his very eyes into a white phantom. She vanished like mist and suddenly was no longer there. The Prince turned and called, but he could not see her, and there was no answer. He was alone in the midst of the silent forest.

From close behind him he heard the sound of human voices. Then figures emerged from among the oaks. It was Jan and the Prince's hunting companions.

'So there you are, Prince!' they shouted. 'We were afraid we would never find you.'

But the Prince gestured to them to be quiet. 'Hush,' he said, 'I want to hear what the white swan is saying.'

They thought he was out of his mind, but at that moment the Prince was listening to a girl's soft voice ...

'Tomorrow I should like to be one of those wax candles in the glittering chandelier. Then, when you held other girls in your arms and danced, my bitter tears would fall on you ...'

The Prince heard no more, and his eyes searched the darkness in vain. His companions tried to distract his attention with jokes and questions.

'Well, Prince, so you never used your arrow?' inquired Jan.

'I shot at the Queen of the Swans, but the arrow returned and pierced my heart,' replied the Prince.

'The Queen your mother will certainly be worried about us,' the old huntsman reminded him, as they mounted their horses at the edge of the forest. In the distance they could see the windows of the castle.

Gradually the Prince recovered his senses. At least he answered sensibly enough, 'My mother will soon cease to worry, when she sees my bride.'

They looked at one another in silence, not knowing quite what the Prince meant. Then they galloped off towards the castle.

The next day preparations for the festive ball kept everybody busy. Towards the evening some people in the village saw a great white swan circle several times around the castle. No one, from that distance, noticed that the swan was wearing a golden crown. The only person in the castle who would see it was the Fool, Tulula. He had already heard whisperings of what had happened the previous evening in the Stone Forest, and had guessed the rest for himself. But he wasn't telling anyone. Who ever listens to a fool's advice?

Everyone else was too busy dressing for the ball to think of anything else. Important guests had been arriving all day. The courtyard was full of carriages, and the servants were busy cleaning the dust and mud from the wheels after the long journeys. Tulula the Fool wandered around in all this muddle, tinkling his cap bells. He kept smiling and peering at the guests, as though he were looking for someone in particular. He spoke to no one, but when he met the Prince's tutor, he permitted

himself some sly remarks at his expense: 'Monsieur Bruyard, I wonder if you realize that you won't have to teach Prince Siegfried French any more?'

'Tut, tut, what's that?' muttered Monsieur.

'From now on he'll be learning another language,' continued Tulula, looking very serious.

'Now, now, and what might *that* be?' asked the tutor, somewhat taken aback.

'The language of the swans. He'll be learning swan talk,' said Tulula, tinkling his bells. 'And that's too pure-white and intellectual for *you*, Monsieur!'

He turned away, leaving the tutor shaking his head in irritation and bewilderment.

Tulula was now in a fine mood. In the gaily decorated hall the long tables were laid in readiness for the banquet. The Fool sat in a corner, teasing the fat Lord Chamberlain. He smiled mysteriously and said in a loud whisper:

'Do you know, my Lord Chamberlain, that there'll be no haunting in the Stone Forest tonight?'

The Lord Chamberlain raised his eyebrows importantly and awaited further enlightenment.

'The wind will be blowing the witches and goblins here to the castle.'

'You've been dreaming again, Fool,' the Lord Chamberlain said, frowning. 'You are talking wildly.'

Tulula persisted in talking in riddles. 'Last night I dreamed about red beards. So look out — that means trouble, my Lord Chamberlain! You know what they say: Red beard, be afeard.'

'It seems to me that some devil has been stirring up the bees in your bonnet, Tulula,' said the Chamberlain crossly. 'People are quite free to have red whiskers if they want to.'

'Ah, but it's *you* who are responsible for everything, my Lord Chamberlain.'

'How is that?' said the Lord Chamberlain, drawing himself up proudly to make it clear he would not allow familiarity.

'It's not too late. Send for three dozen barbers, and have everyone shaved,' Tulula laughed at him. 'Then no one will know who has black whiskers and who has red — nor who was invited and who was not!'

'Be off with you, you wretch!' said the Lord Chamberlain, shaking his fists at him.

Tulula dodged and ran off, shouting from a safe distance, 'If you slip while dancing, mind you fall on your back, Lord Chamberlain. It would be a shame to fall on your lordship's honourable belly and spoil your lordship's very honourable appetite.'

Fools throughout the ages have been able to get away with the most impudent jokes. But there is usually a grain of truth in all their chatter, and the Lord Chamberlain might have guessed that the red beard Tulula was talking about was Redbeard of the Stone Forest.

Later, Tulula was seen to peep into an old suit of armour, which stood in the corner of one of the chambers. In fact, he even whispered something to it, as though the armour had ears: 'Listen, you empty old rattle-bones, be ready. If there's any kind of scuffle tonight, I shall come and hide inside you.'

All that day Tulula the Fool dawdled about from room to room; it seemed as if he were still looking for someone.

At last the ball began.

Thousands of bright candles in the heavy crystal chandeliers were mirrored again and again in the ballroom window-panes. All through the great castle, on the stairs and through the halls, in the gardens and in the stables, there was the hum of voices; servants ran backwards and forwards on busy errands. The cooks and kitchen-maids were red in the face from the heat of the ovens. The Lord Chamberlain strode importantly from room to room, arranging this and that, watching to see that everything was in order.

The young girls the Queen had invited looked flushed and lovely. Their mothers sat fanning themselves and their fathers peeped inquisitively into the dining hall to see the tables laden with delicacies.

At the head of the hall the Queen sat on her golden throne. The young Prince Siegfried stood beside her, looking vaguely anxious as she spoke to him.

'What beautiful girls!' said the Queen with a sigh of satisfaction. 'All of them are the daughters of counts, barons or knights. Does any particular one attract you?'

'I don't know,' her son answered absent-mindedly.

The Queen shook her head impatiently.

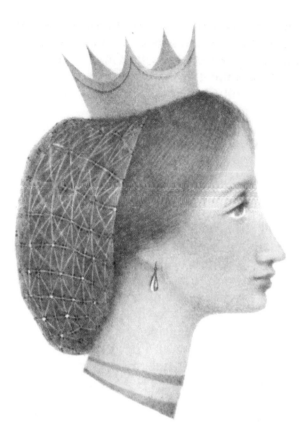

'Siegfried,' she said firmly, 'you must open the ball by asking one of them to dance with you.'

The Prince did not want to dance with any of them. But he could not disobey the Queen and finally he selected a partner. Immediately the ball was in full swing. He danced with this young beauty several times, and her mother immediately began preening herself and behaving as though she were already a member of the royal family. The mothers of the other girls looked at the chosen girl with envy, and their evil looks were like crooked knives.

'Well, son? How did you like Sophia de Villeneuve?' asked his mother, when the Prince finally sat down.

'She was lovely, Mother ... but, somehow she seemed like a greenhouse flower — without fragrance. I bowed and left her ... Oh, what is the use? Life's not worth living.'

'You stupid boy,' the Queen scolded him. 'I can see that I shall have to choose one for you myself. Dance with the dark Elena. What magnificent dark eyes she has! She must surely have Spanish blood in her veins ... Don't delay — go *now* — don't be shy!'

The Prince presented himself to the dark Elena and they danced.

But very soon after he came back to his mother's throne with a miserable face.

'I don't like Spanish wine. I hate that country with its bullfights and scorching sand. What I want is a white, tender smile ... a white flower ... as gentle as swan's down ...'

'Don't go off into a dream, Siegfried,' his mother said. 'Come down to earth and look around you at what is here *now* ...

'There is Marianna de Lorenzo, for instance,' she went on. 'She would please *me* if I were a prince. I would find those blue eyes of hers quite irresistible. Look how gracefully she walks!'

The Prince sighed impatiently. He turned abruptly, chose the nearest maiden and danced. Not long after, he returned to his mother's side.

'Well, my son?' she asked.

The Prince merely shook his head. By now the Queen was really annoyed. She spoke severely:

'Must I remind you why we are giving this ball today? How can you be so stubborn? Go now and dance with Ira van Beck. She will not disappoint you. She is very lively — she will make you feel like a gay village lad at a country dance. Stamp and spring and throw yourself into the dance.'

The Prince obeyed unwillingly. Soon he returned.

The Queen looked at him questioningly.

'I couldn't stamp and spring, Mother. She is full of smiles for me, of course — but I am sure she has two faces; one for the ballroom, another in the privacy of her home ... These beauties all put on fashionable airs — but they could be as graceful as swans, if they were only more natural.'

'What is this constant talk of swans, young man?' his mother said sharply.

The Prince did not reply. What could he say that would satisfy his mother?

But Tulula was never at a loss.

'Just hunting talk, madam,' he said mischievously. 'Your son's a hunter, and swans are a new game!'

110

This remark amused nobody and just at that moment they were interrupted by the Lord Chamberlain. He bowed and said in awed tones: 'A most important guest has arrived, Your Majesty. He is Baron Rotenbart from a distant country, and with him is his most beautiful only daughter, who has turned the heads of half his kingdom.'

'And the other half was mad already,' whispered Tulula the Fool behind his back.

'Mind what you're saying, Fool!' said the Queen, turning to him and speaking in urgent tones. 'We're talking of a more serious matter than you ever worry about.'

'Me worry — just imagine *that!*' cried Tulula so that everybody could hear.

'Worry makes the hair grow white, but mischief makes it red and bright,' he chanted impudently.

Tutula gestured grandly toward the door.

All eyes turned to where he had pointed. At the door stood a red-bearded nobleman with strangely bright eyes, wearing a gold star on his breast. By his side was an unbelievably beautiful, tall girl, dressed in a filmy black gown and wearing a necklace with one large dazzling diamond.

The herald announced their names: Baron Rotenbart and his daughter.

The Prince turned casually to look at them, then suddenly he held his breath: the tall, dark beauty was — Odette!

'Baron Rotenbart has the honour to bow before Your Majesty,' said the Baron, bowing low to the Queen. Then he presented the dark, beautiful girl: 'My one and only daughter, Your Majesty! She was seventeen years of age yesterday.'

The lovely girl curtseyed prettily.

'And my son was twenty-one,' said the Queen, smiling. 'A shared birthday is a very good omen... Now, Siegfried, lead this beautiful girl into the dance!' She added softly for him alone, 'This time it seems I shall not have to press you.'

And ideed this was true!

The Prince whirled the girl off into the dance, forgetting everything else in the world. At last he was happy again, as he had been the previous day in the forest. He was quite oblivious of everybody except his partner. He did not even notice that all the other guests were looking at him in amazement. They stopped dancing and stood around in circle, watching this lovely couple who seemed unaware that they had the floor for themselves. Many of the onlookers stared enviously — if looks could burn, the dancing pair would have felt hot coals showered upon them.

Baron Rotenbart stroked his ruddy beard complacently and could not altogether suppress a malicious smile.

Once more he bowed to the Queen:

'I am quite delighted that my daughter appears to have won the Prince's favour, Your Majesty.'

The Queen too was gazing with pleasure at the Prince and his dancing partner.

'They glide through the waltz like swans on the lake,' she said. '... Ha! Even *I* think of swans now, just like my son.'

'What else would swans be for except for comparison?' murmured the Baron. 'My daughter and I are deeply honoured, Your Majesty.' And as he inclined his head, all the mirrors in the hall seemed to be tinged with red from his reflected beard.

'She will be Queen after me,' the Queen whispered with a sigh, for the thought made

her heart heavy. Her son would be hers no longer.

The Baron heard this remark. A vicious spark kindled in his black eyes and his smile set in a hard line. He glanced at the Queen but she was looking at the Prince and his partner and did not see the expression on the Baron's face. She only heard his honeyed words flattering her son.

As the happy Prince danced, he spoke low to his partner, thinking she was really the girl with whom he had spoken the previous day in the forest.

'Odette, I'm so glad you came!'

The dark beauty corrected him: 'My name is Odile,' she said.

'Really?' said the Prince, taken aback. 'And yesterday I thought you said it was Odette.'

'Yesterday you were a *white* swan,' he continued, as they danced to the light-hearted music, 'and today you're . . .'

'. . . a black one,' finished Odile.

Nothing she said in any way confirmed that they had seen each other the previous evening, and yet the Prince sensed nothing wrong. Indeed, in a very short while he began to think that what had happened the previous evening had been only a dream and that in fact he had never really seen Odile — or Odette — before, only dreamed about her. His memory became confused.

'Tell me, Odile, did we not meet yesterday and talk together?' he asked.

'No. We are seeing each other for the first time now,' said the dark beauty, looking at him so strangely that he trembled. Thus he became convinced that, never having seen her before, he could only have dreamed of her.

'Then yesterday you were only the dream that has come true today.' The Prince laughed. 'The reality is even more beautiful than the dream, and your name sounds even lovelier than before.'

Without noticing that they were dancing, the couple had moved from the ballroom to the next chamber. Through the tall narrow windows it was possible to see the Stone Forest in the distance, the black trees outlined against the clear, dark sky.

'I thought we met there yesterday,' said the Prince, pointing to the faraway forest. 'Is it possible to like that gloomy place? I believe I could — for your sake.'

'It looks frightening, cold and dark,' said Odile. There was a sharp note in her voice as she added, 'But it has nothing to do with me, I assure you, Prince.'

'No, you are here now,' and the beauty of this girl in his arms drove all other thoughts from his mind.

Still holding hands they sank down on a couch side by side, silent, letting their eyes speak for them. The Prince's spoke of love, but what Odile's eyes expressed it would be hard to say. The Prince thought they shone with love — they were certainly very bright. But so

is molten pitch that threatens to splutter and burn whoever comes near.

Black stars fallen into an icy well — that is what her eyes were like. And the black fan with which she fanned herself brought a breath like dark forest air in the dead of night.

The Queen and Baron Rotenbart had watched the Prince and Odile until they disappeared from sight into the next room.

The Baron never stopped paying compliments to the Queen and saying flattering words about the Prince.

It was a pleasure to her to hear him praise the son she loved. He was, indeed, handsome, brave, and in every way worthy to mount the throne. The Baron spoke no more than the truth when he said: 'Prince Siegfried is a fine young man, Your Majesty, a true prince such as every girl dreams of.' And he added, 'My Odile has been longing for such an occasion as this when she would be presented to you, Your Majesty, and to your son.'

'Until now my son had never dreamed of any girl at all,' replied the Queen. 'He thought only of riding and hunting with other young men.'

'That is natural — like every true hero when he is young,' answered the Baron with a smile.

He turned to watch the dancers. 'They really make a very handsome pair.'

By now it was long past midnight. The Lord Chamberlain stepped up to them with a significant smile on his face. 'Your Majesty will no doubt wish to announce the ball is at an end?' he said, 'now that the —'

'— cat's in the bag!' concluded Tulula the Fool just behind him — meddling in other people's conversation as usual.

But the Baron seemed to take it as a joke.

'You've quite a witty fool here, Your Majesty.' He laughed indulgently, and the Queen and the Chamberlain were glad that he had not taken offence.

Tulula, however, took advantage of it.

'It all depends whose bag we mean,' he piped in a thin voice. 'All bags are not alike, are they?' he added — 'any more than all beards are alike.'

'Quite correct,' said the Baron, but he felt annoyed, because there was no telling what the fool would say next, and tonight even when he was not chattering he was performing antics that made people laugh in spite of themselves. At this very moment he was stroking a long, imaginary beard.

The Queen frowned, for the Baron's face became very solemn and grim.

'Clear off, Fool,' said the Lord Chamberlain, waving his arms and driving him away.

But the Baron recovered his composure quickly and smiled again.

'Forgive me, Your Majesty,' he said to the Queen, 'I was forgetting that a fool must make jokes, even though he may have nothing to joke about, poor fellow!'

The Lord Chamberlain sighed in relief. The disgrace that had threatened from the Fool's impertinence had been averted.

'Well, it's not question of how *we* feel, is it, Baron?' said the queen. 'The important thing is what our two children are feeling.' She was happy for her son's sake, and well satisfied with the success of the ball.

While the Lord Chamberlain went off to give his orders to the orchestra and to the servants, the Queen looked towards the room in which the Prince was talking with Odile.

The Baron, watching her, guessed her thoughts — but hid his own.

The ball was coming to an end. The musicians were playing the last waltz.

'Let's dance the last dance together,' said the Prince.

Odile folded her black fan, rose, and went to the window where she stood looking out at the Stone Forest. Her face was a mask.

'It's pretty gloomy out there now, I imagine,' she said. She showed no sympathy for the Prince's memory of yesterday. 'You know, Prince, the uncanny shapes and shadows in a forest at night can make one think of all sorts of strange things. That probably explains your dream of swans — just imagination.'

The Prince peered out into the darkness.

'It was such a vivid dream, it seemed entirely real to me ... But why bother about dreams now? Here the castle is gay and bright, and we are together and happy.'

Odile looked deep into his eyes. 'Yes, Prince,' she said. 'We're not concerned with anything out there. Let the shadows sing their swan-songs — who cares?'

At these words the Prince felt himself pierced to the heart.

Yet still he ignored it and refused to doubt that Odile really was Odette.

They started dancing again and whirled into the main ballroom. There was a hum of hundreds of soft voices. The girl's dancing shoes

rustled over the shining parquet floor. The chandeliers swayed as the warm air rose to the ceiling, and the candles that were still burning now seemed to be flooding over with tears. One of the candles dripped wax right at the feet of the Prince, so that he almost slipped. His heart felt a sudden pang, he did not know why.

'What tiresome candles!' he said impatiently. 'But they cannot stop me dancing with you, my sweet Odile.'

'You pay court so beautifully, my Prince,' sighed the dark beauty. 'I must have many rivals.'

'Not a single one!' vowed the Prince.

'Not even the swan of your dream?'

'Not even her!' the Prince assured her. The previous evening really seemed only a dream now. '*You* are my swan — my *black* swan, Odile.'

At that moment Tulula the Fool came skipping across the ballroom floor, jostling the

couples and jingling the bells on his cap. He called out to the Prince in a piping voice: 'Beware, oh Prince, beware, lest an old red fox cross your path!'

And when the Prince took not the slightest notice of him, he added urgently: 'And a black cat brings ill luck, my Prince!'

But there was no opening the Prince's eyes. He could see and think of nothing but Odile.

Yet Odile heard only too well. She spoke coldly. 'Prince, the time has come for us to say goodbye.'

The Prince was dismayed. 'No, no, Odile, I shall never let you go,' he cried, holding her more closely to him. 'Don't let the chatter of a foolish clown bother you.'

Odile stopped in the middle of the dance.

'Then you mean, Prince ...?' she asked seriously.

'This ball has been held so that I may choose my bride. *You* are the girl I have chosen. I want you to be my Queen.'

'Will you swear then that you have no other love?'

'Of course I swear it!'

And he had hardly spoken when an ice-cold wind blew through the hall and all the lights in the high ballroom suddenly went out. There was complete darkness. Musicians and dancers stopped in confusion.

Then a green light appeared, and in its poisonous glare the speechless guests saw Odile turn from a beautiful, young, seductive girl into a hideous old hag.

She snarled at the Prince: 'You swore! You swore! Now your little white Swan Queen will indeed perish. Her beauty will be no use to her!' She let out a cackle of fiendish laughter.

At the same moment the Queen saw — in place of the refined courtier who had stood before her a moment ago — the hunched and ugly figure of the Enchanter of the Stone Forest. The only thing that did not change was the red beard, but now it was ragged and wild. The threat in his glittering eyes was terrible.

Redbeard did not say a word. He strode up to the frightful old woman who shortly before had looked like a twin of the unhappy Odette, put his arm around her shoulder and stamped his foot. There was a sound of thunder, and the next moment they had both disappeared into the ground.

The strange green light dimmed and went out. Slowly some of the servants recovered from their shock, groped their way to the sconces and relit the candles.

The flickering light revealed older people in huddled groups, and the young men and girls who had been dancing so gaily were clutching each other like statues in attitudes of fright. They looked at each other uncertainly. They were still in a daze and did not understand.

But the Prince understood. He suddenly saw everything very clearly. He realized what he had done to his true love. He knew now that Odile had *not* been Odette — that the 'black swan' had not been the white Queen of the Swans. Redbeard's magic had been powerful indeed! It had deceived the Prince and ruined Odette's hope of ever being released from the cruel spell that bound her.

The unhappy Prince was seized with despair. All he wanted now was to run to the Stone Forest and seek Odette, the Queen of the Swans, whom he truly loved.

Suddenly there were amazed shouts. 'Look! Over there! Outside the window!'

A white swan with a golden crown loomed up behind the pane, casting a white glow in the hall. Then, in the stillness that followed, there was a flapping of wings. Then the white phantom vanished, leaving nothing but empty black night.

'Odette!' the Prince cried after her. 'How could I have forgotten? Odette, forgive me! I shall save you!'

And before the others could restrain him, he flung open the great door and rushed out into the night.

The guests began to recover from their astonishment. They turned to one another with questioning eyes, and spoke excitedly about the strange events of the evening and about the white swan. Some thought the Prince had lost his wits. The Lord Chamberlain had made a clumsy attempt to bar his way. Now he sent some of the servants to run after him — but too late, he was nowhere to be seen.

It was the Queen who looked most stricken. What had she done? What vile and crooked creatures had she been tricked into welcoming into her palace? She spoke fearfully of her unfortunate son. Why had he suddenly rushed away?

Only Tulula the Fool seemed to have any idea of what it was all about.

He said, 'Don't worry about the Prince, good people. At worst he'll merely catch a cold by the lake.'

'By *what* lake, Fool?' the Queen demanded.

And Tulula was forced to tell her what he had guessed: that the Prince must have seen the swan with the golden crown the previous evening. She could be no ordinary swan, of course, but someone transformed and held prisoner by the magic of Redbeard, the Enchanter. Had they not all heard stories of his wickedness and of that uncanny place, the Stone Forest, which everybody shunned? And Tulula had been right in guessing that Redbeard would not leave things at that. Expecting trouble, the Fool saw immediately that the strange nobleman was up to something. And he had distrusted the dark beauty, too, right from the start.

As for the white swan, where else could she have flown to — except to the Stone Forest? And where else would the Prince have gone, except to find her?

The Queen quickly spoke to Jan and his companions. They did not need to be told to follow their Prince and protect him against the magic of the Stone Forest.

'You are his brave and faithful friends,' the Queen said. 'Rescue my son from the malice of Redbeard, and you will earn my love and gratitude for all time. I shall give you a high position in the country.'

'And I'll go with them,' said Tulula. 'And for that I shall need some armour.' And he ran to the suit of armour in the corner of the little chamber.

Imagine his surprise when the armour, at the sound of steps approaching, moved and clasped its hands and begged for mercy in a whining voice. None other than that hero, the Lord Chamberlain, had hidden in there. And so he was taken to the forest too to prove that even though he was afraid, he could still do his duty.

The little procession set off into the night, their weapons glinting in the light of torches.

The Prince's heart was heavy as he rode toward the Stone Forest. How could he have been so blind! It was love itself that had blinded him: no trap could have been more deadly than the one that Redbeard had set for him. What hope was there now?

He tied his horse and began to run through the trees. He stumbled in the dark, but was sure of the way.

He searched all around the lake, but there was no sign of the swans. So he ran to the clearing, and there a lovely young girl appeared. He was about to shout for joy when he realized it was not Odette but one of her companions. Behind her came another graceful girl, and another: before long the whole company of them stood there, released for the moment from their swan spell.

The Prince, hidden, watched them impatiently as they danced, as light as mist.

They were very beautiful, but none was as lovely as Odette. None of them had such golden hair, nor did they dance and move as lightly as Odette.

He longed for Odette. He waited and waited, hoping to see her, but she did not come. Had they lost their Queen? The Prince was gripped by a terrible fear. Finally he could bear it no longer and ran out from the thicket towards the dancers.

Startled, they ran away. Their dance became a panic-stricken flight to the lake. There, in a moment, they turned into swans again. One by one they slipped from the banks onto the water's surface, like boats with white sails and glided away into the silvery darkness.

Oh, where was Odette? He was alone again with his fear. His eyes tried to pierce the gloom.

Was there a sound? No, only the beating of his own heart. There was total silence all around him.

Then he saw her!

She was hurrying through the forest towards the lake. The golden crown glittered on her shining hair, and suddenly the whole clearing seemed radiant with gold.

'Odette!' he cried, springing into her path with outstretched arms.

Odette held out her hands to him. 'This is the last time we shall see each other,' she said. 'I came to say goodbye, for you are so very dear to me.'

'Why can we not be together?' said the Prince, overcome with grief. 'Can you not forgive me for my dreadful mistake? It is *you* I love — *only* you.'

'You gave your promise to the other one, Prince Siegfried.'

'I thought I was giving my vows to *you*.'

'Yet she had a different name.'

'A name like yours.'

'But not the same. You should not have forgotten so easily,' she said gently.

'I believed that I had only dreamed of you and that I was meeting you in reality for the first time there at the ball.'

'You believed a trick,' she said sadly. Her eyes filled with tears. 'She is cunning, that jealous Odile.'

'Who is she?'

'That was Walburg — a sorceress in league with Redbeard. Did you not realize that Baron Rotenbart was none other than Redbeard, the evil lord of the Stone Forest?'

'My poor Odette! What a terrible wrong I have done you!'

'I watched you through the window. I knew that Redbeard would win. Now the two of them are gloating over us, for they have destroyed our happiness.'

'No, Odette, it cannot be so!' cried the Prince. 'I made a mistake, but it was not a betrayal. I was confused by the likeness.'

'Not a betrayal... no, my Prince,' said Odette sadly. 'But it is too late.'

'I was confused — but for love of *you*,' maintained the Prince. 'She was so like you, though she did have black and not golden hair — and dark eyes, not blue ones. I saw you twice over, the way we sometimes see two moons, one in the sky and one in the surface of a lake. That was how I saw you — once in reality and the second time in my heart.' He buried his head in his hands. When he looked up again there was such anguish in his eyes that her heart went out to him.

'I so longed for you,' he said, 'that I saw you in the counterfeit picture of you. Please forgive me!'

'I have already forgiven you.' She smiled

Odette burst into tears. 'Oh, my love, you have indeed freed me from their power — but through death! The crown protected my life. Now I shall surely die!'

All the colour drained from her cheeks and the strength from her limbs. She wavered and fell like a broken flower. The Prince caught her in his arms.

'I shall save you! I shall fight for you!' he cried.

'Watch out, dear Prince. The vengeful owl is here already!' whispered Odette. 'As soon as it has the golden crown in its claws I will die.' She pointed at the branches of a huge oak tree. The owl swooped across the lake and seized the golden crown in its talons.

The Prince ran to the shore, ready to plunge into the lake and snatch the precious crown. But the owl flew high above him and disappeared into the depths of the forest.

The Prince turned back to Odette and found her lying motionless in the grass.

She was as white as snow, and her breathing was growing weaker.

'Odette, my darling, you must not die!' He knelt down beside her and kissed her, but her cheek was cold. It was like kissing a marble statue. He was in despair. He could not face the world without Odette. Tears ran down his face.

He rose and stared down helplessly at Odette's still body lying in the grass. Her face looked like white marble and her golden hair was spread on the ground. The moon's rays seemed to cover her with a cold white shroud.

He stood there, lost and hopeless.

'You fool!' a harsh, derisive voice behind him hissed. 'You thought you could get the better of me, did you? Run away from here if you value your life!'

He turned and saw Redbeard. His face was hideous and his evil, glinting eyes were as black as night.

The Prince stood firmly in his path. Never was a man more glad to face his enemy! At last the Prince could fight for his love.

'I am not afraid of you, Redbeard! I shall fight you for Odette's life. Release her, coward!' he commanded. 'Bring her back to life!'

'Get out of my forest!' roared Redbeard. 'You have no business here. This is *my* kingdom.'

with tears in her eyes. 'But I shall have to leave you.'

'No, no!'

'It is not in my power to change or break the spell the Enchanter put upon me. His trick succeeded.'

'But my love *is* pure and true,' cried the Prince in despair.

'Farewell, dearest one,' whispered Odette. 'I shall be changed back into a swan — but this time for ever.'

'I shall break that accursed witchery!' shouted the Prince. In his anger he tore the golden crown from her head, thinking that this might prevent her being changed from her human form back into a swan. Odette was unable to stop him. He threw the crown far out across the lake. It sailed through the air and fell on the water's surface. But, strangely, it did not sink.

The Prince stared in alarm.

'I am challenging you, Redbeard!' the Prince shouted at him. 'Give Odette back her life or I shall kill you and cut your heart out.'

'I've warned you, it is *you* who will die!' said Redbeard, hurling himself at the Prince.

But the Prince was ready for the attack. He stood his ground and threw himself into the fight with a desperate courage.

Love gave him strength and cunning. He was agile and as tall as his enemy, but Redbeard was very strong and sprang with the force of a tiger. They fought for a long time. Redbeard kept trying to seize the Prince's throat with his claw-like hands, but the Prince forced him to loosen his hold and threw him to the ground. More than once he pinned the Enchanter down on the moss. But Redbeard was as lithe as a snake. He twisted and turned and escaped the Prince's hold, then with a sudden lunge came at him with renewed hatred.

The Prince resisted him, and again he had Redbeard on the ground, pressing him deep down into the moss. At last Redbeard's strength was giving out. He begged for mercy and tried to trick the Prince by promising him half his kingdom. But the Prince still held him down and would not relax his grip.

Then Redbeard offered him his entire kingdom — all his underground treasure, and the secrets of his witchery and potions. The Prince was not interested. He was fighting to save Odette.

With one last hefty blow he struck the magician dead and tore out his heart. He gripped it in his hands and felt them go cold. It was not a human heart he was holding but an icy stone.

With a shudder he threw the heart of stone into the lake.

The Enchanter was dead, and the fight was over. The mysterious owl flew down from the trees carrying Odette's golden crown in its claws. The owl settled beside Redbeard's lifeless body and placed the crown over the wound in his chest, hoping its magic would bring Redbeard back to life.

But something very different happened.

The Prince was about to snatch the crown away, but the moment it touched the dead sorcerer's body it flared up with a green flame and the owl and Redbeard dissolved into dust.

A fierce wind rose and scattered the black and red dust, leaving no trace of those two evil beings. The power of evil in the Stone Forest was broken.

The Prince had won, but Odette was dead. He knelt by her side to kiss her for the last time. A gentle breeze was moving the branches which had been still for so long. The forest seemed to stir with life again. Suddenly — he caught his breath — surely Odette was still alive!

She opened her eyes and looked at him with loving recognition. A blush crept into her cheeks and she whispered, 'Dearest one, you have saved me with your love.'

'You're alive, you're alive!' cried the Prince, overjoyed. He pressed his face to hers as though to hasten her return to life with his own warm breath. He felt his heart might burst!

Odette looked around her with wonder, as if awakening from a deep sleep. Her eyes sparkled. She was free!

'You rescued me,' she kept repeating gratefully.

He took her hands and kissed them. 'My love, you'll no longer be a Queen of Swans — you will be a Queen of people. We shall be happy together for all our lives.'

She gazed up at him, smiling, her heart too full for words.

'I shall fill this forest with cheerful creatures,' he went on, 'with singing birds and squirrels, with pretty fawns who will eat from our hands, with shy foxes and badgers. There shall be no more sadness to remind us of your enchantment.'

Odette suddenly looked alarmed. 'My companions,' she said. 'What has happened to them?'

'There they are.'

They turned to face the group of lovely laughing girls who came running to Odette and joyfully embraced her.

Day was dawning as they made their way through the wood. 'Prince, Prince!'

Loud calls and the sound of a horn rang through the forest and they met Jan and his fellow-huntsmen running to meet them, with Tulula and the panting Lord Chamberlain behind.

It was a joyful reunion.

One of the young men went ahead with the glad news. The others followed, Odette riding with the Prince, Jan riding beside them and listening to the strange tale of the enchanted swans.

The Queen was watching for them on the battlements. Torches still burned in the early morning light as a last reminder of that terrible night which had ended so well. With great joy she welcomed her brave and triumphant son and his beautiful Odette — not just a chosen queen but a bride won from death by the power of true love.

The Firebird *was first performed by Diaghilev's Ballet Russe in Paris in 1910. It was Stravinsky's first ballet score and he wrote it in close collaboration with the choreographer, Mikhail Fokine. Fokine himself appeared in the first performance in the role of Ivan Tsarevitch.*

The idea for the ballet had been Fokine's. He had wanted to choreograph a 'Russian' ballet, choosing for the story several of the works of the Russian writer Afanasiev, including The Tale of Ivan Tsarevitch *and* The Bird of Light and The Grey Wolf. *He took elements of the stories to suit his purpose and the result was the enchanting tale of a prince who captures*

a magical firebird. In exchange for her freedom, she gives him a feather which will bring her to his aid if ever he needs help.

The ballet has been popular in the United States since before Fokine's death in 1942. A version by George Balanchine using designs by Marc Chagall was in the repertoire of the New York City Ballet for many seasons.

In Britain, The Firebird *was first produced in 1942 with Margot Fonteyn in the title role. She was coached by the great Russian dancer Tamara Karsavina, who had danced the part in the original production.*

The Firebird

Once upon a time, in a land far away, there lived a King and Queen who had a little son named Ivan.

Prince Ivan was not like other boys. His arms were of gold to the elbows; his legs were of silver to the knees. By day, in the sun's glow, his forehead was golden; by moonlight it was silver.

One day the old nurse was rocking the little Prince to sleep, but he would not close his eyes. So she called the Queen:

'Come, Your Majesty, come and rock your baby to sleep.'

The Queen sat down beside the cradle but she had no more success than the nurse. So she called the King:

'Come, Sir, come and sing your little son to sleep.'

The King sat down beside the cradle and began to sing a lullaby which told of a fabled bride who would one day be Ivan's — a princess described in riddles to which there was no answer:

> *'Sleep, little son, and slumber long,*
> *Grow through boyhood tall and strong.*
> *Into the great world you shall ride*
> *And win a princess for your bride —*
> *The lovely Princess Vasilissa,*
> *Daughter of three mothers,*
> *Darling of three grandmothers,*
> *Sister of nine brothers.*
> *Her beauty dazzles like the sun*
> *Rising from the sea.*
> *You shall strive till she is won*
> *And she your wife shall be.'*

The little Prince soon fell fast asleep, and he slept for nine years, nine months, nine weeks and nine days.

When at last he woke he turned to the King and said: 'Father, I shall go out into the world to seek my bride, the Princess Vasilissa, daughter of three mothers, darling of three grandmothers, sister of nine brothers, a princess whose beauty dazzles like the sun rising from the sea.'

The King was astonished. 'You are too young to have learned much wisdom, my son,' he cried. 'I am afraid you will get lost or die on the way.'

But Prince Ivan answered his father: 'I am clever enough and old enough. All I want is your blessing so that I can go out into the world and bring back the lovely Vasilissa. If you give it then I shall go, if you do not give it, then I shall go just the same. Do as you wish.'

'Wait, my son, wait at least so that I can measure you to see if you are strong enough,' said the King, and set about measuring Prince Ivan, who proved to be neither too fat nor too thin, but just right.

Whether they wanted to or not the King and Queen finally gave in and consented to their son going to seek his bride.

Taking a handsome horse from the stable, Prince Ivan harnessed him with a Tartar saddle of tooled leather and a silver bridle,

pulled the silken girths tight and adjusted the
stirrups. When all was ready he leaped up onto
the saddle and rode away.

The Prince rode through woods and across
fields, through villages and towns, wherever
the road took him, until he came to a big dark
forest. And there, beside the road at the edge
of the forest, he saw a bush which was burning
fiercely. Underneath the bush there was an
anthill, and as the sparks dropped on it the
ants scurried back and forth with their eggs,
frightened out of their wits. When they saw the
Prince they cried out:

'Oh help us, Prince Ivan, help us! Otherwise
we shall all burn to death, our eggs and our
babies too!'

Quickly Prince Ivan jumped down from his
horse, cut the bush off at the roots and put the
fire out.

'Thank you, Prince Ivan, thank you,' said the eldest ant, coming up to him. 'In return we shall give you a word of advice.'

'Well, that is always welcome,' said Ivan with a smile.

The ant continued: 'Never, Prince Ivan, never turn back until you have come to the end of your journey.'

Prince Ivan thanked the ant but he shook his head and thought to himself: 'That is a strange piece of advice, a really strange piece of advice. Why, I've set out on this journey to bring back Princess Vasilissa and I am not likely to turn back without her when I'm only halfway there.'

So Prince Ivan rode on, over hill and over dale, through deep forests that seemed endless,

of the water he saw a fish flopping on the sand. It had been tossed up by the waves and could not get back by itself.

'Help me, Prince Ivan, help me!' begged the fish. 'Throw me back in the sea, otherwise I shall die.'

At these words Prince Ivan jumped down from his horse, grasped the fish by the tail and threw it back into the sea. A moment later the fish's head appeared above the water.

'Thank you, Prince Ivan, thank you,' it called. 'In return I shall give you a word of advice.'

'Well, that is always welcome,' replied the Prince.

'Listen, then. Never let what you have caught slip out of your hands.'

Prince Ivan thanked the fish but thought to himself: 'That is strange advice, really strange advice. Why, I've set out on this journey to win Princess Vasilissa and I am not likely to let her go once I have won her.'

And so Prince Ivan rode on and, after crossing the sea, came to a high mountain on which

grew a large oak tree. At the foot of the tree were two young ravens who had fallen from their nest in the branches of the tree. When they saw the Prince they squawked and cried: 'Help us, Prince Ivan, help us or we shall die. Our parents have flown away and left us to fend for ourselves. But how can we find food when we don't even know how to fly? Give us something to eat, or we shall die of hunger.'

Prince Ivan quickly jumped down from his horse, hid in the bushes and took careful aim at a deer that ran by. He killed it with one arrow and the ravens had more than enough to eat.

'Thank you, Prince Ivan, thank you,' cried the ravens joyfully when they had eaten every scrap. 'In return we shall give you a word of advice.'

'Everyone wants to give me advice, even ravens who are too helpless to get food for themselves,' said the Prince with a wave of his hand.

'You should take it seriously,' said the ravens, 'and listen carefully to what we tell you. Never refuse the request of a friend.'

'A good piece of advice that, but not very clever,' said the Prince to himself. 'I helped the ants when they asked me and I helped the fish and the ravens and they were not my friends. So naturally I would help anyone who is my friend.'

No one knows how long Prince Ivan went on his way through the world, but one day he came at last to a city that was draped all in black.

Dismounting at an inn, Prince Ivan entered and asked the innkeeper: 'What has happened? Why is your city draped all in black?'

'Ah, you must be a stranger if you don't know about the tragedy that has happened here,' replied the innkeeper. 'Our King's only daughter has disappeared — no one can find her. That is why the city is in mourning.'

'What is her name?' asked Prince Ivan.

'Her name is Vasilissa,' replied the innkeeper. 'She is the daughter of three mothers, darling of three grandmothers, sister of nine brothers. And her beauty dazzles like the sun rising from the sea.'

Prince Ivan was overcome with despair at these words. The only reason why he had set out on his long journey across the world was to find the beautiful Vasilissa and take her home to be his bride.

Without a word of farewell to the inkeeper he mounted his horse and rode away to the castle.

The King was surprised to see such a handsome youth, wearing a fine cape and fur-edged cap with tinkling golden bells; a youth, moreover, with arms of gold to the elbows, legs of silver to the knees, and the golden sunlight glowing on his forehead. The King's surprise was even greater when Prince Ivan declared that he had come far across the world to find the lovely Vasilissa, his own beloved daughter, to take her home with him as his bride.

'You may have my daughter,' said the King. 'I shall be glad to give her to you. But first you must find her, for she has disappeared.'

'I shall find your daughter,' Ivan replied. 'I shall find her if I have to go to the four corners of the earth.'

And so Prince Ivan set off on his search. Over hill and over dale he rode, through deep forests and wide spreading plains, across rivers and dry prairies. He asked everyone he saw on the way if they knew anything of the beautiful Princess Vasilissa, but he always met with a sad shake of the head.

He began to give up hope that he would ever find her. 'What is the point of wandering aimlessly about the world when I don't even know where to look for Princess Vasilissa? It would be better to go home to my parents, and marry some other princess.'

He was just about to turn his horse and go back the way he had come when he remembered the ants and their advice never to turn back until he had come to the end of his journey.

'Perhaps it was good advice the ants gave me, after all,' he said to himself, and rode on. 'I will persevere.'

One day towards evening he came to a large garden full of flowers and trees and luscious fruit. He was so tired, however, that he tied his horse to one of the trees, lay down on the grass and fell fast asleep.

He did not know how long he slept, but suddenly he was woken by the sound of soft music. He rubbed his eyes and looked up at the branches of the tree above him, outlined against the night sky. They were covered with magnificent golden apples and it was these apples which gave out the lovely music as they swayed in the breeze. He got up and stretched out his hand to pluck one of the apples. At that very moment the whole garden was filled with a murmuring sound as if swept by a gentle breeze, and bathed in a bright glow like the first rays of dawn. The light was not from the sun, however, but from a strange bird with golden feathers. It perched high among the branches and began to eat the golden apples.

'What a beautiful bird,' sighed Prince Ivan.

He stood still in wonder at the beauty of the scene before him.

Then the bird sang in a voice like golden bells:

'How sweet are these apples,
These golden apples,
Sweet as the smile of
Princess Vasilissa,
Daughter of three mothers,
Darling of three grandmothers,

Sister of nine brothers.
Her beauty dazzles
Like the sun
Rising from the sea.'

As he listened to these words Prince Ivan's attention quickened. The song continued:

'How sweet are
These golden apples
Sweet as the smile of
Princess Vasilissa,
Who was carried away
By the deathless magician:
Beware of Kostchei
Who lives on the blood
of those who intrude
Where dwells the Princess
Who longs to be free.'

Prince Ivan stood rooted to the spot, but before he could pull himself together the bird sang again:

'How sweet are these apples,
These golden apples,
Sweet as the smile of
Princess Vasilissa
Whom Prince Ivan seeks
By day and by night
In darkness and light
On land and at sea.
He'll find her where'er she may be.'

At this the Prince jumped up into the tree and seized the golden bird, for clearly this magnificent creature could help him.

'Now I've got you, I'll never let you go!'

The golden bird dug its claws into Ivan's silver legs and beat its wings against his golden arms, trying to free itself from his grasp. But Ivan held its wings fast with his hands, and soon had it firmly in his power. Then the bird, seeing that it could not get free, said in a pleasant voice:

'Let me go, Prince Ivan — you won't regret it if you do. I will tell you where you can find Princess Vasilissa — and if you listen to what I tell you, you may succeed in rescuing her. I am the Firebird, and I alone have power over the magician Kostchei the Deathless, who kidnapped the Princess and holds her here in his black castle. Let me go and I will advise you what to do.'

The Prince was about to let the bird go when he suddenly remembered the fish's advice never to let what he had caught out of his grasp.

'It was good advice the fish gave me, after all,' he said to himself, and strengthened his grip on the beautiful bird. Then he said to the Firebird: 'It is true that I am young, but I have grown a lot and I have learned much, too. I do not need advice from you — I have had plenty of that already; but help is something no one has been able to give me. So I cannot release you.'

'You speak wisely, Prince Ivan,' said the Firebird. 'But let me go. Pluck a feather from my tail and keep it with you. Whenever you need help all you have to do is to wave it above your head and I shall come.'

'Very well,' said Prince Ivan. 'Put your wise and lovely head on my broad shoulders and guide me with all your knowledge and wisdom.' With that he plucked a golden feather, then tossed the bird high into the air, where it vanished.

'Well, we shall see if the Firebird meant what it said,' thought Prince Ivan. And he lay down beneath the tree and fell asleep again.

He slept until daybreak and he would have slept longer, had he not been woken by the voices of young girls chanting a sad tune. Ivan rose quickly to his feet and he saw thirteen beautiful girls coming towards the tree with the golden apples where he had been sleeping.

The Prince was overwhelmed by their beauty, and the appearance of one of them — the thirteenth — completely took his breath away, for she was more beautiful than all the others.

The Prince stepped towards her and said: 'Tell me, beautiful Princess, who are you, and how do you come to be here in the garden of the magician Kostchei the Deathless?'

The lovely girl answered in a sad voice: 'I am the Princess Vasilissa, daughter of three mothers, darling of three grandmothers, sister of nine brothers. I did not come here willingly, but was brought against my will by Kostchei the Deathless, who wants me to be his bride.'

She looked at Prince Ivan with tears in her eyes, and went on: 'But what about you, my lord, why are you here? Men do not dare to

come here, nor even wild animals and the evil
ravens. Go quickly! Do you not know that the
terrible magician Kostchei lives here? He
catches whoever sets foot in this garden, and
sucks his blood to the last drop. That is why he
lives forever.'

'I know that, beautiful Vasilissa,' said Prince
Ivan. 'But I shall not leave! I have come to free
you from this wicked magician. I am Prince
Ivan, and you have been destined to be my
bride since the day I was born. I have come to
take you home with me!'

'Whatever your destiny may be, Prince Ivan,
I am doomed, for no one — not even you —
can free me from my fate. Kostchei the Deathless is strong and powerful. Go! Go, while
there is still time!'

Prince Ivan, however, would not let himself
be frightened. Instead, he sat down in the
shade of the tree and drew Princess Vasilissa
down beside him. While the twelve other girls

picked the golden apples, they sat and talked together, and the hope grew in their hearts that perhaps Prince Ivan really could overpower the magician.

Suddenly the sky darkened as a huge black cloud covered the face of the sun. The Princess leapt to her feet and she and the other girls had gone before Prince Ivan realized what had happened. There before him stood the powerful Kostchei himself.

The magician was a repulsive old man with a toothless mouth that stretched from ear to ear, and a horrible, crooked nose. He was quite bald except for one single hair on the top of his head. He wore a black cloak and carried a long stick. His black eyes blazed with hatred.

'Greetings, Prince Ivan,' he said with a croaking laugh. 'I know why you have come. You wish to take the beautiful Princess Vasilissa away from me!'

'Yes, I do,' replied the Prince.

'You are neither the first nor the last to try... I shall give you three tasks. If you fulfil all three, Vasilissa shall be yours. If you cannot, you shall never leave here alive.'

'I shall perform the tasks,' answered the

Prince, 'and then we shall see who is the better of us two.'

'Now listen carefully,' said Kostchei the Deathless. 'Behind my castle is a forest that is one mile long and one mile wide. By tomorrow you must fell the trees, cut the wood into logs, dig up the roots, plough the earth, sow wheat, reap it, thresh it, grind it, and from the flour bake *pirozhki* for my breakfast. If you do this, I shall give you your second task; if not, you know what your fate will be.'

And with these words the magician was gone.

With a heavy heart Prince Ivan sat down under the tree.

He thought with longing of all the things he would never be able to enjoy now, of the warm sun and the gentle rain he would never feel again. 'What can I do?' he cried in despair, for he knew he would never be able to fulfil the task the magician had given him.

But as he sat there under the tree thinking of his fate he suddenly remembered the Firebird's promise. Drawing out the golden feather from inside his coat, he waved it high above his head. At once the garden was filled with a murmuring sound, as if swept by a gentle breeze, and bathed in a bright glow as if the magician's castle was on fire. Then the Firebird alighted on the tree.

'What do you want, Prince Ivan?' it asked.

'Oh, Firebird, it seems as if I am doomed and I don't know if you will be able to help me,' said the Prince. 'Kostchei the Deathless appeared to me, and has given me three tasks. If I fulfil them, the beautiful Princess Vasilissa will be mine. If I cannot, I shall never leave here alive. The first task I must finish by tomorrow. I must fell the forest behind the castle, cut the wood into logs, dig up the roots and burn them, plough the earth, sow and grow and harvest wheat, thresh it, grind it, and from the flour bake *pirozhki* for the magician's breakfast. How can I ever do that?'

'Oh, but Prince Ivan,' replied the Firebird, 'that is nothing. Do not worry, everything will be done in time. Now go to the castle and cheer up the lovely Vasilissa; she is weeping because of you... Then at midnight come to the forest behind the castle and you shall see.'

The Firebird was gone in a flash, leaving the Prince alone once more.

So Prince Ivan made his way to the castle. It was all black — outside and inside. The walls were black, the furniture was black, and even the light coming through the windows was dark. But when Ivan found his beloved Princess, everything seemed to be full of light. This might be the last evening they would ever spend together, but the shadow of this thought only made their joy seem brighter.

At the stroke of midnight Prince Ivan went out at the back of the castle. He could not believe his eyes! Instead of the thick forest in which he had so recently stood he saw a field of stubble strewn with piles of logs and sacks of flour and a huge fire in their midst where the remaining tree stumps were burning. There, looking on, stood the Firebird.

'See, Prince Ivan, everything is ready,' said the bird gaily. 'As for the *pirozhki*, the lovely Vasilissa will bake those for you.'

And with these words the Firebird leaped into the fire. In an instant all that remained of it was a pile of ashes.

Prince Ivan was shocked to see such a beautiful bird die. Then he became frightened of the thought of the remaining tasks he would have to perform without the help of the Firebird. Surely all was lost! But just then the Firebird stepped out of the ashes alive and even more beautiful than before.

'You seem surprised, Prince Ivan,' it said. 'But this is why I am called the Firebird. I bathe in fire just as you bathe in water. When you come out of your bath you are clean and handsome, and when I arise from my bath of fire my feathers are more glossy and I am more beautiful than ever before.'

Prince Ivan watched the Firebird fly away, then, in high spirits, carried the sacks of flour to the castle where Princess Vasilissa began making the delicious little pancakes, *pirozhki.*

In the morning Kostchei the Deathless was astonished to find nice hot *pirozhki* on the table for breakfast. When he looked out of the window and saw that the forest had been felled he was furious.

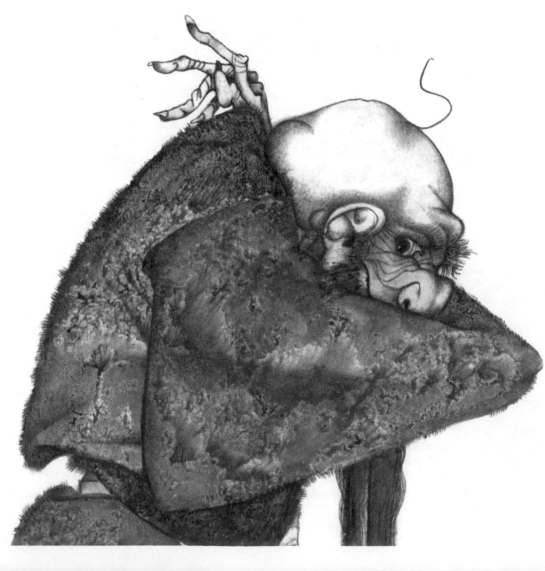

He said: 'You have fulfilled the task this time, but there is a harder task to come. By tomorrow morning you must dig a lake behind the castle seventeen miles long and seventeen miles wide and so deep that not only small boats but great galleys will be able to sail there. You must fill that lake with water, build across it a bridge with a gilded rail and on that bridge plant an apple tree every three yards so that one blooms and the next bears apples. Nor may they be ordinary apples: they must be golden ones, with pearls instead of seeds — the kind the Firebird likes to eat. Underneath each tree there shall be a spring of fresh water so that when I go for a stroll I shall be able to sit and rest in the shade and have a drink when I'm hot and thirsty. If you do this, I will give you your third task; if you do not, you know what your fate will be.'

So saying, Kostchei the Deathless departed.
This time Prince Ivan was not as sad as the
day before. Again he waved the golden feather
above his head. At once, as before, there was
a murmuring sound like the passing breath of
a breeze, and everything glowed with a bright
light as if the castle were on fire, and the Firebird suddenly appeared from nowhere.

'What is it you want, Prince Ivan?' it asked.
'Were you given a new task?'

'Yes, I was,' replied the Prince. 'This time
I am to dig behind the castle a lake seventeen
miles long and seventeen miles wide and so
deep that not only small boats but great galleys will be able to sail there. And I am to fill
that lake with water, build across it a bridge
with a gilded rail, and on that bridge I am to
plant an apple tree every three yards so that
when one blooms, the next bears apples...

Nor may they be ordinary apples, but golden ones with pearls instead of seeds — the kind you like to eat. Underneath each tree there is to be a spring of fresh water so that when the magician goes for a walk he will be able to sit and rest in the shade and have a drink when he is hot and thirsty.'

'Oh,' said the Firebird, airily. 'That's nothing. Just leave it all to me and everything will be ready by morning. Now go and cheer up the lovely Vasilissa. She is weeping because of you.'

Prince Ivan thanked the Firebird and went to find Princess Vasilissa. She was sitting, sad and forlorn, by the window, but she soon smiled when she saw the Prince.

As dawn broke the Prince looked out of a window. There, glittering in the morning sun behind the castle, he could see ships sailing on a huge lake. Across the middle was a magnificent bridge, and on it apple trees — one in bloom and the next covered with golden apples. In a row all along it underneath were springs gushing fresh water.

Overjoyed at the sight, Prince Ivan made his way to the garden.

After a while Kostchei appeared and when he saw the lake he exclaimed in anger: 'So you have fulfilled the second task also! But you needn't be so happy about it, you haven't won yet! Today I shall give you the third and most difficult task. Listen carefully... By tomorrow you must bring death to me!'

'Why wait until tomorrow?' said Prince Ivan with a laugh, 'why not now?' And with that he drew his sword and struck the magician a blow on the head.

But the sword bounced off as if the head were made of steel and Kostchei cackled; the Prince was helpless.

'You've forgotten that I am Kostchei the Deathless! You cannot bring death to me, Prince Ivan! For *that* you will lose your life!'

Then the magician waved his hand and Prince Ivan was instantly surrounded by fire and smoke and horrible monsters, headless ogres, ugly witches, lizards, devils and dragons, all roaring and shrieking as they flung themselves on the poor Prince.

Prince Ivan fought with all his strength, but all his skill and courage were no match for the horrible monsters. He cut the lizard in half, but immediately in its place there were two. He cut the dragon's head off with one stroke, but in its place there were two. He pierced the giant through, but another giant leaped out of the gaping wound. The battle seemed to be hopeless.

Then the Prince again remembered the Firebird. He reached for the golden feather and waved it high above his head. At once there was a great gust of wind and a bright glow filled the air, and there beside him stood the Firebird with a golden sword in its claw. Brandishing it, the Firebird cried: 'Take heed, Kostchei the Deathless! Your death is near!'

Hardly were the words spoken when all the horrible monsters, headless ogres, devils, witches, lizards and dragons disappeared into the ground. The magician turned pale and began to quake with fear.

Passing the golden sword to the Prince, the Firebird commanded: 'Quickly now, Prince Ivan. Take the sword and cut me in half. Inside you will find a large black egg, and inside that will be the death of Kostchei the Deathless.'

'I cannot do that!' cried Ivan. 'You have helped me so much — how can *I kill* you?'

'You must do as I tell you,' cried the Firebird. 'Otherwise it will be the death of you. I have carried that egg inside me for a long, long time and I cannot lay it. That is why the magician kept feeding me with golden apples to keep me alive, preserving the egg of death where it could not harm him. Cut me in half, take the egg out and break it. Come, Prince Ivan, do it quickly!'

At this point Prince Ivan remembered the two ravens and their advice never to refuse the request of a friend. So taking up the sword, he cut the Firebird in half and the egg inside as well. There was a deafening roar and Kostchei the Deathless fell to the ground dead. The slain bird's body burned with a bright flame till only ashes were left. Then out of these the Firebird stepped again, alive and more beautiful than ever. Soaring high into the air, it circled twice above Ivan's head, a golden cloud in the sky, then it was gone and was seen no more.

The moment the magician was dead unusual things began to happen in his black castle. The darkness vanished, the walls turned red, the furniture blue, the dishes silver. All the rooms were filled with light and movement, and Prince Ivan was suddenly surrounded by a hundred knights whom Kostchei had killed and who had now come to life again.

These knights were followed by the twelve beautiful girls held prisoner there by the magician. Then came the loveliest of them all: Princess Vasilissa, daughter of three mothers, darling of three grandmothers, sister of nine brothers, her beauty dazzling like the sun rising from the sea. All of them, gay and happy, thanked Prince for having freed them.

The knights then brought a saddled horse and Prince Ivan lifted Princess Vasilissa up on its back. Then he laid the beautiful leather saddle on his own handsome horse, looped the silver bridle over its head, pulled the silken girths tight, adjusted the stirrups, leaped into the saddle and off they went.

They journeyed for many, many miles, high and low, over mountains and valleys, over fields and meadows, through forests and clearings, across streams and rivers, until finally they came to the city ruled by Vasilissa's father, the King.

The people quickly took down the black cloth which draped the whole city and replaced it with cloth of red, for the beautiful Vasilissa had returned to them with her bridegroom, Prince Ivan. When the King saw her he wept tears of happiness and so did her three mothers and three grandmothers and nine brothers. Then there was great feasting and rejoicing, the like of which no one has seen or ever will see. After the old King died the land was governed wisely and well by King Ivan and Queen Vasilissa until the end of their days.

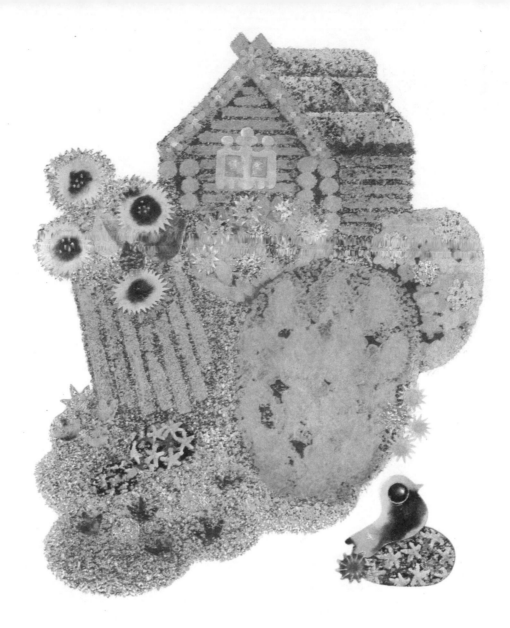

Petrushka *was the result of the collaboration between three of the greatest men involved in twentieth-century ballet, all of whom were working under the influence of Serge Diaghilev, founder of the Ballet Russe.*

Diaghilev presented Petrushka for the first time at the Châtelet Theatre in Paris in 1911 with the fabulous Polish dancer Vaslav Nijinsky dancing the title role. The three men who were responsible for Petrushka were Mikhail Fokine the choreographer, Alexandre Benois the designer, and Igor Stravinsky, the composer.

The ballet is based on an old Russian folk tale about a showman and his three puppets: Petrushka, the Ballerina and the Moor, who steals the Ballerina from Petrushka and then kills him.

After it was first staged in Paris, it was performed all over the world. Benois redesigned the ballet several times, including the production that was mounted for American Ballet Theater in New York in 1942.

The first British company to stage the ballet was the London Festival Ballet in 1950, with Anton Dolin in the title role. Margot Fonteyn danced the role of the Ballerina when the Royal Ballet premièred their production in 1957.

Petrushka

over, and Petrushka was washed to the very edge of the puddle and close to the stove.

'There, you see, Grandma, he wriggled out of *that*, didn't he?' said Mishka, laughing. 'He got wet but finished up right by the stove!' He helped his Grandmother wipe the floor, while Petrushka sat drying.

There was always lots going on in that house. During the day there was the smell of cooking and baking, and the merry music of a harmonica to dance to. The evenings were the best time of all, when bearded men and plump women came to sit round the table and tell stories. Petrushka listened spellbound till his tired eyes closed in sleep.

Five kittens lived up in the loft, four females and a tom. Mishka had found them abandoned in the street one cold winter's day. He had taken them up to the warm loft and looked after them well, taking fresh milk every day and playing endless games with them.

Petrushka the rag puppet belonged to a small boy called Mishka. It was such fun living with Mishka in the small wooden house that Petrushka didn't mind at all being tossed about during their rough games.

Mishka and the puppet were romping about when Grandmother appeared at the door. 'Do you know,' she said, 'I pricked my finger when I was making your puppet! That means he'll have more than his share of bad luck.' She smiled fondly at Petrushka. 'But he has a happy mouth, so he'll probably wriggle out of any corner.'

Mishka was hopping round the table on one leg, shouting: 'He will wriggle out of anything, Grandma!' when he tripped over a bucket and splashed some of the water out of it. Petrushka fell from his arms right into the wet. Then Mishka slipped and knocked the pail right

160

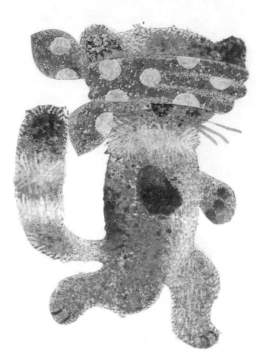

through the front door into the street he met Alexander, who was waiting for him just round the corner. They set off together in the bitter cold, hoping they would somehow find their way to St Petersburg.

They wandered for several days and nights, getting lost in the snow, until at last they reached a small deserted hut. 'Let's stop here and have a good rest,' said Petrushka.

But when morning came Alexander wasn't keen on moving from the shelter of the wooden hut, so Petrushka set off again alone.

As he trudged wearily through the snow he heard some bells ringing. Soon a horsedrawn sleigh came into sight. As the mare trotted through the snow whirls of frost crystals flew from her hooves.

'Why, I know that man holding the reins,' thought Petrushka happily. 'He used to visit us sometimes in our wooden house. He loved Grandmother's cakes and he had a loud laugh that made the whole house shake!'

Then one sad day in the early autumn, Mishka was sent away to school in St Petersburg. It seemed as if he forgot all about his rag puppet. As time passed Grandmother grew old and frail. The kittens grew up and four of them moved next door. Only the grumpy tabby tomcat called Alexander stayed.

Soon after this a strange man came to the house. He had bushy eyebrows, sharp, greedy teeth, and breath that smelled of beer. The moment he entered he began to shout that the house was his, that he had bought it and everything in it. He didn't want the tomcat Alexander around, so he shoo'd him roughly away. He said even Petrushka was his and grabbed the poor puppet by his legs, letting him hang head downwards till finally he dropped him on the floor.

That night Petrushka decided it was time to leave. He would try to find his way to St Petersburg to look for Mishka. As he slipped

'Mister, mister!' shouted the puppet, but the man heard nothing through his thick fur cap.

However the mare must have seen him, for she slowed down so that Petrushka could climb onto the sleigh. He hid himself in a sack of poppy seed at the back of the sleigh, sheltered from the sharp wind.

Petrushka fell asleep at once. He was woken by the sound of voices, the banging of doors...

'Well I never, what have we here?' said a strange voice. An exploring hand fished the sleepy Petrushka from inside the sack. 'Katya, come here quickly! I think I have a new playmate for you!'

So this was how Petrushka came to live with the carpenter and his little daughter. The old man with the fur cap had left the sack of poppy seed in exchange for an oak chest. He never saw the puppet, for he didn't open the sack,

just set it down on the bench and drove away.

Many years went by, Katya grew up and spent her time going for long walks and dreaming of boys instead of playing with Petrushka. But they were still the best of friends.

One day Petrushka watched Katya's father hang a beautiful sign that Katya had painted outside his carpenter's shop. It said:

NEW TABLES AND CHAIRS
ANY REPAIRS.
COME TO THIS SIGN,
THE BEST WORK IS MINE,
TAKE A SEAT,
IN COMFORT EAT,
IN COMFORT STAY
OUT OF THE WAY.

Petrushka liked best of all the line which

said 'stay out of the way.' How true it was that there was always someone, somewhere, in someone else's way. If a tramp sheltered for the night in a cellar, he was in the way of a policeman. If a poor woman came to the farm to do some weaving, the four children who came with her were in the way. The gipsies who stopped on the village green, the foreigner from another country, the feeble old lady, they were all in someone's way.

Petrushka made up his mind, right then, that it was time to move on. Next time the peasant woman came to the shop with her four children he crept up to the smallest one and said: 'Would you like me to live with you?'

The little boy's face lit up with pleasure. 'Oh yes!... but they will never let you go,' he said sadly. He lifted up the puppet to have a better look, and dropped him right into some glue which the carpenter had been using to stick a bow together for the woman's herbs.

'Here's my chance,' thought Petrushka. As quick as lightning he jumped onto the woman's shawl and became well and truly stuck! The woman set off home with her children without realizing that Petrushka was there.

And that is how Petrushka arrived at his new home.

Petrushka made himself useful whenever he could. The woman, Anya, worked in other people's houses, doing their weekly wash. If anyone seemed unwilling to let in her four children, the hidden puppet would murmur, 'What's this? Disgusting behaviour! Let them in at once or your house will be turned into an old woodshed!' The scared householder, not knowing who had spoken, would then open the door wide and welcome the children, and give them nice things to eat.

One day they went to the flea market. There you could sell any old thing that you didn't want — moth-eaten hats, nails and screws, cracked plates, buttons and shoes...

Petrushka had a brilliant idea. Wherever they went, the puppet would look down from the bundle on Anya's back and point out any thing he saw that could be sold in the flea market.

'A painted metal button by your left heel! A strong piece of wire to the right! An earthenware mug, slightly cracked, with a red handle

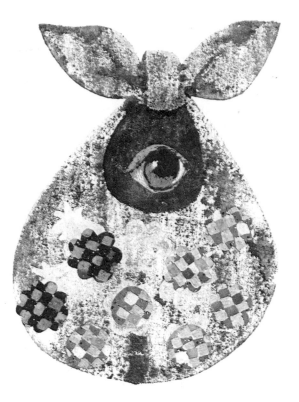

'Where did you find him? Tell me! He is one of my puppets!'

Poor Anya, speechless with fright, looked on helplessly. Petrushka wriggled free once and would have tried to lose himself in the crowd, but the hateful hand reached out and closed around him once more.

The man stormed at him: 'You can struggle and whine as much as you like, it will do you no good. You're mine and I shan't let you get away this time.'

Now the smallest boy and Petrushka were both crying loudly.

'What is all this noise about?' A policeman hurried up, scowled at the big bully of a man, then inspected Petrushka suspiciously. He swayed importantly on the heels of his enormous boots. 'Let's have the truth now! Does this puppet belong to you or does he not?'

'He most certainly belongs to me,' growled the man, but Petrushka kept shaking his head pitifully, as if pleading in protest.

behind that birch tree! I believe you'll find it doesn't even leak!'

When they had found enough things to sell, they returned to the flea market, spread them out on the shawl, and Petrushka would shout as loud as he could to attract people to come and buy.

People laughed and crowded round. The shawl was soon empty.

One day they were arranging their poor goods on the shawl, when a large figure suddenly loomed over Petrushka. 'Do my eyes deceive me? Blood and thunder, this puppet belongs to *me!*'

Petrushka recognized the voice of the man who had taken possession of Grandmother's house. A big rough hand closed tightly around the puppet's leg and lifted him high in the air, scattering the goods clumsily all over the place.

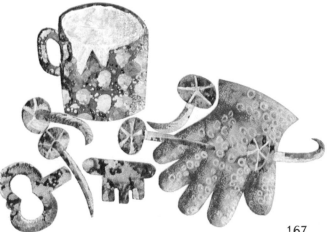

167

'Why is he shaking his head then? He keeps on shaking his head...' stammered the policeman.

The man answered slyly: 'Why, he's only made of rags! He doesn't know anything. He can't think or feel. But let me introduce myself, Inspector. I am the Puppet Master.'

'A Puppet Master...? And a rag puppet... it stands to reason they belong together...'

So Petrushka was left in the choking clasp of the Puppet Master, while Anya with her children disappeared as if the earth had swallowed them up.

'You are going to act in a theatre,' said the Master to the puppet. 'People will be hysterical with laughter when they see your silly nose, and that worried look in your eyes.' The man forgot to add that he would make sure Petrushka had plenty to look worried about.

Then the puppet was thrown into the wooden box which became his prison and his room, his cage and his shelter. He was in the power of the Puppet Master and had to do all that he said.

Petrushka became the clown in the puppet show. At every performance he was knocked about unmercifully for everyone to laugh at. Afterwards the Puppet Master threw him back in his box and set off once more.

They were always moving from place to place, and at last one day they arrived in St Petersburg, the city Petrushka had so longed to see! He had forgotten by now why he had wanted to go there, but he felt very excited.

The box hit the ground with a jolt, and before the puppet realized they had actually arrived, he heard children crowding around, jumping up at the little theatre and shouting. The dark ceiling over the puppet's head was flung up and Petrushka, still confused by all the noise and commotion, jumped high into the dazzling light, turned head over heels and landed right on the stage. The children shrieked with delight.

Then he saw the great buildings, the lights, the noisy crowds in the snow. The play had begun.

There were many visits to St Petersburg after that first one and it was always just as exciting.

By now Petrushka had got to know the other puppet performers who acted out their lives on the stage. And he had fallen in love with Holubichka, the dainty ballerina. She would tiptoe in, wafting a cloud of lavender scent around the doting Petrushka. 'I ache all over,' she would complain, stretching and arching her back, and shaking her beautiful head. She would twirl around Petrushka so that her silky hair brushed him as she passed. He only had time to blink with delight before she proudly danced away on her points.

She never even noticed Petrushka. It was always the same. He would be left looking after her in dazed admiration, while she cared nothing for him.

Another of the puppets was called the Grinning Terror. He was a skeleton with wide jaws gaping in a ghastly smile. The old puppet had been with the Puppet Master for many years. Until the skeleton's joints grew stiff with age he played in the theatre. If the play was about fighting he was always there when someone got killed. He cut them down with his scythe. But in time he became too worn out, and the Puppet Master pushed him behind the props and told him to sit still and be quiet. The Grinning Terror wasn't at all happy with this arrangement.

One day the Skeleton was grumbling more than usual about the Puppet Master again.

'That silly old fool! How dare he say that I am too old to act in a play! How can a *skeleton* grow old? Tell me that!'

'Of course you can't grow old,' stammered Petrushka, full of sympathy, 'I really can't see why you can't play sometimes, just occasionally...'

'But I want to act *today*,' insisted the Grinning Terror in a voice so fierce and threatening that Petrushka really began to feel scared. He could not help wondering why the Skelet-

on was suddenly so insistent on playing *today*.

The great square of St Petersburg was humming with all the noises of a winter fair. Children with their parents or nursemaids gathered excitedly round the toy stall, the roundabout and the coconut shy, marvelled at the dancing bear, the tumblers, the musicians, the man with the long beard and the Cossack soldiers. The little theatre stood in the centre of the square.

'Ladies and gentlemen, come closer, gather around,' shouted the Puppet Master. 'Come nearer,' he roared above the loud music of the fair. 'Come and see the dark and handsome Moor perform feats of prowess, and prove his strength!'

The red curtains parted, and on the stage stood the dark and handsome Moor, a magnificent turban on his head.

'There he is, there he is, now you see him, folks.' The Puppet Master kept up his patter.

'The Moor is a valiant warrior,
Bold and defiant,
He has the eye of a hawk,
The strength of a giant!'

The Moor flashed his white teeth, clenched his fists and stretched out his powerful muscular arms. He really was an imposing puppet!

He picked up a large coconut, raising it slowly till he held it steady high above his head. He did this three times to prove his strength, then tossed it up and caught it. At that moment the scene was suddenly transformed into a green oasis in the parched desert, with palm trees swaying in the breeze; somewhere in the foreground flashed the gleaming eyes of a leopard. The children gasped with wonder.

Before the crowd had time to recover from their astonishment, the beautiful Holubichka tiptoed onto the stage, dressed prettily in a stiff tutu skirt.

The soldiers whistled with delight, the nursemaids giggled and the rest of the audience held their breath in anticipation. The backdrop kept changing so that one minute the scene was a desert, the next minute a jungle, the next a snowy plain with a ringing of sleigh bells to make it even more real.

Then the Puppet Master shouted:

'Here's a chap who's queer in the head,
Perhaps he bumped it when he fell out of
bed!'

as poor Petrushka tumbled onto the stage, and fell flat on his face. Everyone roared with laughter. But Petrushka uttered a piercing wail. The Puppet Master jeered at him, then in a tearful voice mimicked the poor puppet.

While the Puppet Master made fun of Petrushka, whining and pulling faces, Holubichka and the Moor continued to dance merrily around him. The audience shrieked with laughter.

'Just look at the ballerina, she has eyes only for the Moor!'

These lines were Petrushka's cue to start jumping around and acting the clown, sobbing pathetically. But it seemed as if he had forgotten his part. A curious feeling had come over him: instead of acting like a puppet, as people expected him to, Petrushka suddenly felt that he was something more than that. There was a strange fluttering sensation in his chest. Could a rag puppet have a heart?

Petrushka opened his eyes and seemed to see clearly for the first time. Why was it always *he* who got the knocks and the Moor who danced with Holubichka? And did she *enjoy* dancing with that clumsy creature, or did she only pretend to?

'Come on, Petrushka, act the clown!' the people cried impatiently. But Petrushka sat as if in a trance, his thoughts all over the place.

So the scene came to an abrupt end and the Puppet Master drew the curtains together. He grabbed Petrushka by the scruff of his neck, and threw him angrily into his box, slamming the lid over him.

Petrushka felt himself. Nothing was broken. He was all in one piece. But how he longed for Holubichka!

'At least I can *think* of you, Holubichka!' sighed Petrushka. 'No one can stop me thinking of you.' Sitting in the corner of his box he lost himself in day-dreams.

'Dear Holubichka, you are as pretty as the blossom in spring time. If only I were as strong as the Moor! Then I could look after you and protect you. If only I were as powerful as the Puppet Master, then I would climb with you in

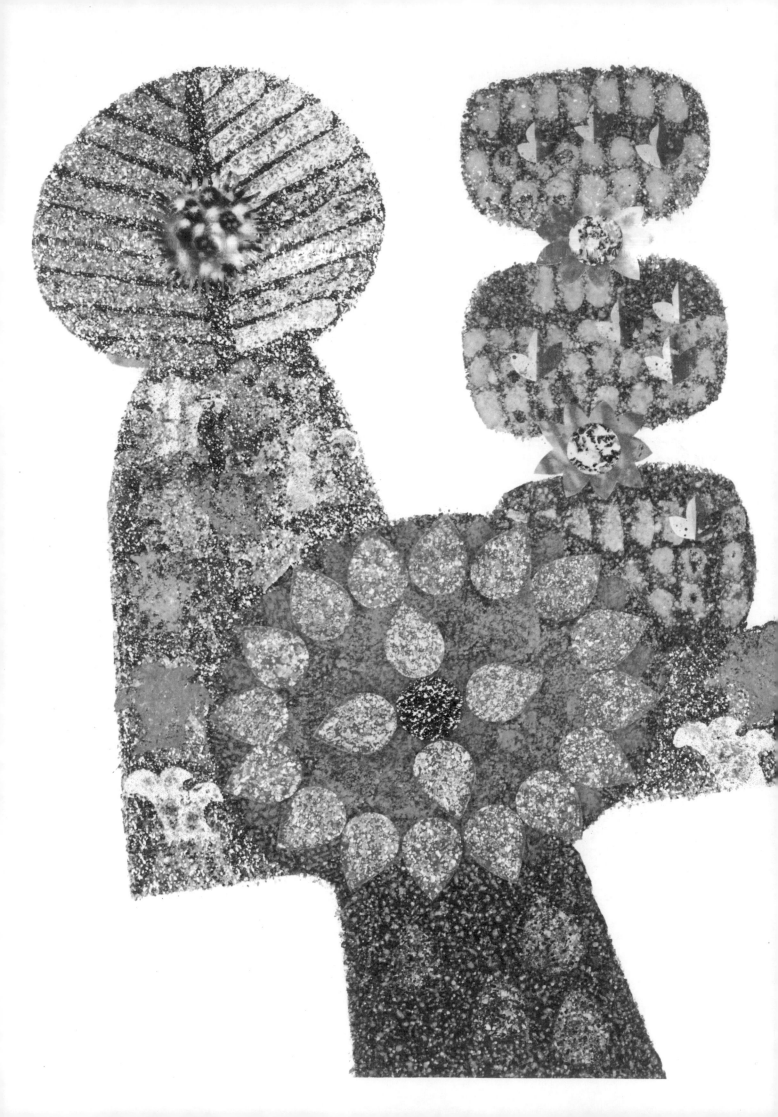

my arms to the top of the highest tower of the town. I would lift you up and set you high above all of St Petersburg. You would shine there, like the moon! People would stare and say: that is not the moon, that is our beautiful, shining Holubichka!

'But I am *not* big and strong, I am not powerful, I am just nobody.' Petrushka sighed and at that moment he became aware again of that fluttering in his chest, as if a butterfly were trapped inside his chest...

At last Petrushka fell asleep. He dreamt that Holubichka was by his side; that they had loved one another for a long time and had no secrets from each other. Holubichka caressed his face with her soft hands, kissing his unlucky nose, and said; 'Of course, I dance with the Moor, but all the time my thoughts are with you! Fancy you thinking I like the Moor, what a ridiculous idea! That horrid conceited show-off, he's as fat as a barrel!' Then she faded from his dream.

Petrushka tried to call out to her to wait — to stop a minute — but no sound came from his straining throat. 'Please wait,' his heart was calling, but the ballerina had gone and he woke up.

'I must see her, I must know what she is doing. She can't, she must not, be dancing again with the Moor!'

He looked up in despair at the lid above him, and through a small crack of the box he

saw the gleam of the Puppet Master's evil, mocking dark eye, shadowed by its bushy brow, staring down at him... The unhappy puppet hid his own eyes with his hands. 'This man lives for only one thing; to trap me, hold me and imprison me... without mercy, without compassion...'

While Petrushka sat dreaming in his box Holubichka was dancing. 'Is there anyone as pretty as I?' was the only thought in her head as she whirled around the stage with the Moor. 'No one has such a perfect, porcelain complexion!' Proud of herself, Holubichka jumped higher and higher. The Moor clasped her tightly as they moved faster and faster.

'How beautiful I must look in contrast to the Moor! He is so fat and I am so dainty,' thought the conceited Holubichka as she greedily listened to the applause of the audience. 'How they must love me!'

Everyone watched the wild, rhythmic dance in wonder. 'That ballerina is practically *flying* through the air,' exclaimed a young man, and another said; 'The Moor's belly is bouncing up and down like a balloon!'

'How closely together they dance,' a nursemaid said.

'If Petrushka saw them...' said a child's voice.

Holubichka heard, and paused a moment. 'He would be so unhappy that he would cry,' thought the ballerina. 'He has always been so kind to me... no one else is kind. The Puppet Master is mean, and as for his... his Grinning Terror, when that ugly old creature stares at me, I go cold all over. But Petrushka is not afraid of him! He is nice to him, and when I am with him I am not afraid either. Petrushka is the kindest one of all...'

The ballerina's day-dreaming came to an end, for the Moor grabbed her again and lifted her so high that she shrieked with delight and forgot everything except the wild, dizzy whirl of the dance.

Among the props stood Petrushka watching, as white as a sheet... He had raised the lid and climbed out of his box.

So great was Petrushka's longing for Holubichka, and his hatred of the Moor, that he had decided to challenge him. Whatever happened, it could not be worse than being a clown, always being laughed at.

It was dusk, and although snow was gently falling, the crowd in the square was bigger than ever. The Skeleton crawled out of a dark corner, and came creaking and rattling to Petrushka's side.

'Just look at those two, how closely they hold each other! Look how they gaze into each other's eyes!' he wheezed maliciously. 'What about it, Petrushka, shall we go out onto the stage and join the act?'

But Petrushka heard nothing. Tortured by jealousy and love, he was aware only of two pairs of hands embraced in the dance. The tiny white pair were his, *his*... his heart cried in anguish.

The despairing Petrushka threw himself upon the stage and pounced on the Moor. Holding him by his shirt he shook him wildly, while the bewildered Moor wondered what on earth had happened. He stumbled awkwardly all over the place, gazing around stupidly.

'Just you wait!' shrieked the puppet into the Moor's ear. 'You think you can do what you please because you're so big! You think I'll always crouch in a corner, stay silent and put up with everything, looking on while you dance with Holubichka! You're wrong! I'll give you such a thrashing!' and Petrushka's small fists pummeled away furiously at the Moor.

Only then did the Moor come to. He rolled his eyes, blinked, took a deep breath and lashed out against the nearly exhausted little puppet.

The onlookers held their breath ... the terrified ballerina rushed between the rivals, imploring them to stop.

The Moor did stop for a moment, glaring at the ballerina, who collapsed wordlessly at his feet. Then, flashing his eyes, he raised his strong arms and bore down upon Petrushka.

'Help!' shrieked the crowd.

'Run away, Petrushka!' shouted a child.

But just then the Moor, grunting like a crazed animal, grabbed the puppet and hurled him off the stage.

'Oh, gracious!' exclaimed a nursemaid. 'Poor Petrushka, he threw him out like a rotten apple!'

The men laughed. 'Poor Petrushka, a rotten apple!' And one of them threw him back onto the stage.

The Grinning Terror, agog with excitement, hobbled onto the stage, his bare skull shining in the frosty night, his mouth agape in a sickening smile. His old bones clicked as he clapped his hands in glee.

The Puppet Master watched with satisfaction — the unexpected performance was a great success. He took a sip from a bottle of vodka, gulping it loudly, then turned back to look at the excited faces of the audience.

The terrified ballerina slowly awoke from her faint and saw the Moor with a sword in his hand. She jumped quickly to her feet.

'Moor, please stop, please wait!' she begged, vainly trying to hold him back with her little hands, to bar his way...

'Oh, look! Look! What a scene! The Moor, fighting our little ballerina!' hooted the crowd.

But the Moor shook himself free from Holubichka and brandished his sword above his head. Consumed with rage, he darted at the puppet who defied him.

'Run — RUN, Petrushka!' cried a little child. 'He has a sword!'

The puppet ran for his life, while the Moor followed furiously, slashing the air with his sword. The people were enjoying themselves. None of the spectators took the chase seriously, they were all laughing and shouting. No one tried to stop the Moor. They were all teasing Petrushka, mocking him, thrusting sticks in his way. When he tried to run off behind the curtains, the Puppet Master barred his way. The Skeleton stood by, silent and waiting.

There was no escape. Petrushka was cornered, and at the Moor's mercy. He saw the blade of the sword flash, then down it slashed — and pierced the puppet's heart. The unhappy ballerina uttered a tragic cry and fell beside him.

As Petrushka lay mortally wounded, scenes from the past came back to him. He saw the faces of all the people most dear to him: Mishka, Grandmother, and Alexander the Tomcat; the mare and the man with the thick fur cap; Katya and her father the Carpenter; Anya and her four children.

Then his eyes misted over and all the faces were blotted out...

'He won't get up! Tell him he's *got* to get up!'

'On your feet, Petrushka! Come and make us laugh!'

'It's just a joke, isn't it?' a child said, uncertainly. 'He's all right, isn't he?'

But the puppet lay perfectly still.

The cry went up, 'He is dead, he has been killed!'

Soon the children were all sobbing: 'Petrushka! Our Petrushka!' An icy wind ran through the fair and the crowd began to break up, shivering. They looked at each other, puzzled, as they moved away with their weeping children. Why had it gone so cold all of a sudden? And who had upset the children with that talk of killing? 'How ridiculous! You can't *kill* a puppet!'

Then waves of other people who hadn't seen the show surged forward towards the little theatre, demanding to know what had happened.

'You actually *saw* someone killed?'

'Who?'

'Petrushka the puppet, Petrushka the clown...'

'What a thing to happen!'

The Puppet Master mumbled under his breath and waved his bottle of vodka, while his constant companion, the Grinning Terror, gazed eagerly at the people, and at the puppet.

'What's going on here?' demanded a policeman who had suddenly appeared on the scene.

The Puppet Master rolled his eyes, and picked up the lifeless body of the little rag puppet.

'What a lot of fuss about an old rag puppet,' babbled the Puppet Master, his tongue thick with drink: 'Made of rags... just rags... any old rags...'

Soon the people drifted away to other parts of the fair to enjoy themselves. They started to munch sweets again, and sing and throw streamers. After all, this was the fair, and they had come to have a good time.

180

Nobody suspected that, hidden in a dark corner of the little theatre, the Grinning Terror was clapping his decrepit bony hands with joy, muttering to himself, 'What deadly fun I have had today!'

'Here I am! Here I am!'

What was that? Everyone looked up. Somebody was shouting from the roof of the theatre. Who could it be?

'Look! There he is! He didn't die, he's alive!' someone shouted.

'Who?'

'Petrushka, of course! Hi there, Petrushka!'

The Puppet Master looked up in alarm. What were these people saying? Here was the broken puppet in his hand ... and yet ... there was Petrushka, alive and laughing, on the theatre roof! Was it a ghost? He shuddered and let the rag body slip slowly from his grasp.

The man felt giddy. He tried to run away, but he staggered and fell. Suddenly he felt a stab of pain in his hand. The Skeleton's scythe had cut his flesh. While the Puppet Master lay cursing the whole world, the Grinning Terror clattered away and was lost in the darkness.

And above the fair, Petrushka, the irrepressible, brave Petrushka, danced and sang as he always would. His spirit would never die. Petrushka would live in the hearts of the children of St Petersburg forever and ever.

182

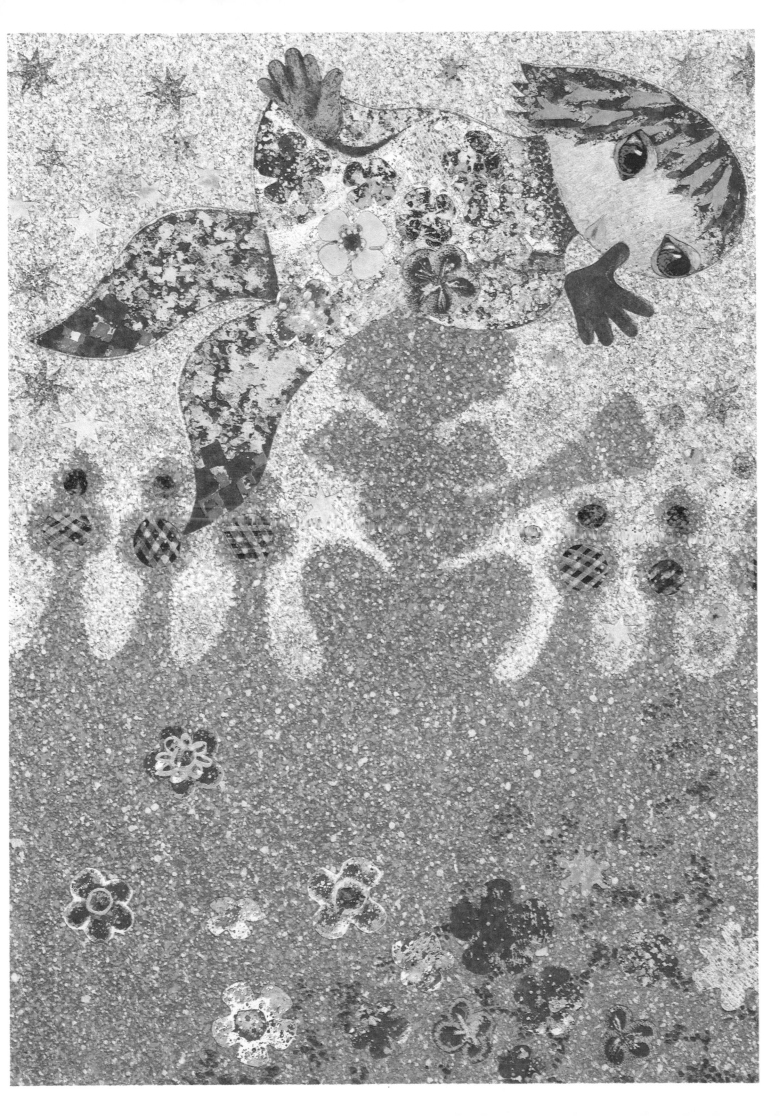

Cinderella *is possibly the best-known and the best-loved fairy tale ever written and it is not surprising that there have been many ballet versions of Charles Perrault's classic story.*

The earliest one was produced in the King's Theatre in London in 1822, with music by Fernando Sor and an Italian ballerina, Maria Mercandotti, in the title role. More than seventy years later, in 1893, the Russians staged their version of the story in the famous Maryinsky Theatre in St Petersburg. The Italian, Pierina Legnani, danced the part of Cinderella, with choreography by Lev Ivanov and Enrico Cecchetti. They used music by Boris Schell.

The music that is used today was written by Serge Prokofiev and was first used in the production staged by the Kirov Ballet in 1946.

Two years later Sir Frederick Ashton staged his famous production for the Royal Ballet in London. Moira Shearer and Michael Somes danced the principal roles, with Ashton, himself, and Robert Helpmann creating memorable ugly sisters. Seventeen years later, Ashton and Helpmann teamed up again; this time their down-trodden step-sister was the enchanting Margot Fonteyn.

Cinderella

Once upon a time there was a rich nobleman who lived in a lovely castle with his pretty wife and his beautiful daughter, Rose.

They all lived happily together and it seemed that nothing in the world could spoil that happiness. But one day Rose's mother suddenly fell sick. As every day went by she became more and more ill and although the nobleman saw to it that his wife had the best possible treatment, it was to no avail and his good wife eventually summoned her husband to her bedside.

'I am dying, husband, but before I leave you, please promise me one thing.'

'Anything, dear wife,' replied the husband.

'It will not be good for Rose to be without a mother, so, please promise me that you will marry in a year and a day's time.'

Her unhappy husband gave her his word and indeed, in a year and a day's time he married a poor widow with two daughters of her own, Agatha and Adele.

'Now my darling daughter will not only have a mother but two sisters as well,' said the husband to himself. 'Perhaps she will stop grieving her late mother so much.'

But the nobleman had made a disastrous mistake. The poor widow was mean and selfish and her two daughters were even more spiteful, arrogant and mean than she.

It was with some relief that he went away on a long business trip in a far-off land believing that Rose would be cared for in his absence.

However, as soon as the nobleman's back was turned, Rose's two stepsisters and their mother turned their spite on Rose and treated her very badly. They took all her beautiful clothes and jewellery away from her, leaving her nothing but sackcloth to wear.

Rose's stepmother was so mean that she sacked the servants and made Rose do all the work instead. All day, Rose would cook, make the beds, do the mending and clean out the fires. The fire cinders used to make her so dirty that the stepsisters mockingly called her Cinderella. Poor Cinderella was even banned

from her pretty room and was forced to sleep in the scullery under the staircase with nothing to eat but stale bread.

Cinderella longed for the return of her father and never gave up the hope that one day all would be well again.

While Cinderella sat day-dreaming about how she would like things to be, in the royal palace in the city someone else was also day-dreaming. It was the Queen. She was wondering how long it would be before her son, the handsome Prince Cornelius, would fall in love and get married.

'All he seems interested in is hunting,' complained the Queen to her husband. 'One day he'll have to rule the land and he won't be able to do that if he's in a forest hunting.'

The King only sighed and shrugged his shoulders.

'I know,' said the Queen excitedly. 'We'll hold a grand ball at the royal palace and invite the daughters of all the noblemen in the land. Our son will then surely meet a beautiful girl and fall in love.'

The Queen was very pleased about her idea and lost no time in sending out all the invitations.

The very next day the invitation arrived at the nobleman's castle and the two stepsisters ·were beside themselves with glee, waving the

invitation at poor Cinderella. 'Of course, it's no good you going to the ball, Cinderella. Who'd want to dance with a raggledy-taggledy like you!'

Cinderella sighed. How she wished she could go to the ball. But Cinderella had no more time to think about it — she was kept far too busy and the whole castle was caught up in a hive of activity as the two stepsisters prepared for the great day.

Day and night dressmakers were busy sewing exquisite robes of silk and brocade for the two stepsisters. The shoemaker and hatmaker were busy too, while all the two ungrateful sisters could do was complain to the craftsmen or grumble even more at Cinderella when things were not going quite right.

At last the day of the grand ball arrived. The two sisters were up at dawn, ever since when the nobleman's castle had been practically bursting with activity.

The dressmakers were fitting the dresses. The shoemaker was finishing the shoes. The hatmaker was starching the bonnets. The goldsmiths were polishing the jewellery. The stable lads were grooming the horses. The coachman

was washing the coach. The stepmother was shouting orders and the two sisters did not give Cinderella one moment of peace with their constant cries of 'Get me this, Cinderella,' or 'Bring me that, Cinderella,' or 'Don't stand around doing nothing, Cinderella.'

Finally, the stepmother and her two daughters were ready to leave for the ball and when the coach rattled away from the court Cinderella slumped on to a stool by the kitchen stove and sighed: 'Oh, how I would love to go to the ball if only for a minute or two.'

No sooner had she uttered the words when the kitchen was flooded with light and there stood before Cinderella a most beautiful lady.

'I am your fairy godmother,' the beautiful stranger said to Cinderella. 'I am here to make your dream come true. You will go to the ball of your dreams.'

'Oh,' cried Cinderella. 'I do so want to go.'

'Then fetch me a pumpkin from the garden,' ordered the fairy kindly.

Cinderella was puzzled but did as she was bid.

The fairy touched the pumpkin with her wand and it turned into a shining coach.

'Now fetch me the mousetrap,' said the fairy.

Cinderella returned with the mousetrap which contained six white mice and a fat rat.

With another touch of her wand, the fairy turned the six white mice into six gleaming white horses and the fat rat into a plump, jolly coachman.

Cinderella skipped with glee as she gathered up the six green lizards that the fairy had asked for next.

These the fairy godmother promptly turned into six liveried footmen.

'Oh, how wonderful,' cried Cinderella. 'I'm beginning to believe that I really will be going to the ball, though I fear the footmen and driver are better dressed than I.'

'Do not doubt that you will be the most beautiful girl there,' said the fairy and she waved her wand again.

Immediately there appeared many fairies of the spring, summer, autumn and winter, bringing clothes, jewellery, a veil and everything that a rich noble lady needs when she attends a royal grand ball. Everything was so fine and beautiful, of such delicate and exquisite materials and colours that it was like a dream.

When Cinderella was dressed at last, the fairy godmother gave her a pair of dainty glass slippers for her feet.

The fairy looked at Cinderella and smiled. Then she pointed sternly at a large clock hanging above the mantelpiece and said: 'Have a wonderful time, but mind you are back here by midnight, or there will be trouble.'

Cinderella looked at the clock. It was not yet eight. 'I have lots of time,' she smiled.

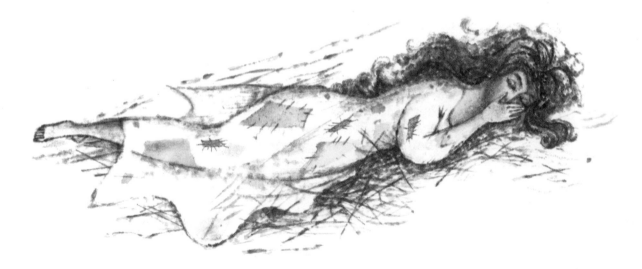

Then Cinderella was driven quickly to the royal palace in the city.

The ball at the royal palace had already started. The music was gay and everybody was dancing or laughing. Only the Prince looked bored ... but that was until he saw Cinderella enter the room.

Cinderella stood in the doorway. She looked so beautiful that every head turned to her, including her spiteful stepmother and two step-sisters. Even the King and Queen could not help but admire the lovely stranger in her exquisite dress, woven as if from the very rays of the sun and studded with diamonds of the clear summer night sky.

The enchanted Prince made his way through the crowd of ladies, bowed to the beautiful girl and for the rest of the evening, never left her side. They danced only with each other and neither had eyes for anyone else. Yet, no mat-

ter how hard the Prince tried, he could not make the beautiful girl reveal her name or where she lived.

'When the time is right, you will know, my Prince,' Cinderella smiled in reply and the Prince did not ask again.

There were jealous mutterings among the other ladies who each dreamed that the Prince would fall in love with their own daughter. They tried all kinds of tricks to lure the Prince away from Cinderella, but so wrapped up in each other were the handsome couple that they were oblivious to what was going on around them.

The Queen beamed happily as she watched her son falling in love with the beautiful girl. She was proud of her cunning idea and kept nudging the king: 'What did I say? Wasn't I right?'

The Prince and Cinderella danced so much that soon they were hungry and sat down at the laden table. It was a long time since Cinderella had seen so many delicacies and she pecked at this and nibbled at that while the Prince watched her admiringly.

Then Cinderella was back in the Prince's arms once more and being whirled around the dance floor.

But the time was flying by and Cinderella hadn't looked at a clock. It was only when she heard the palace clock chiming midnight that she realized her promise to her fairy godmother and rushed from the startled Prince's arms into the dark night outside.

Cinderella raced down the long marble staircase losing one of her glass slippers on the way and was just in time to see six little white mice and a fat rat scampering away from a large pumpkin. Six green lizards gazed at her and with a faint rustle, Cinderella's wonderful dress changed into tattered rags.

Choking back a sob, Cinderella raced through the streets of the city until she reached her father's castle.

Breathless and exhausted, she sank on to the kitchen stool staring at the one remaining glass slipper in her hand — all that was left of the memorable evening.

Cinderella quickly hid the treasured slipper and had no sooner done so than her step-sisters arrived home.

The two sisters were jubilant as they related the evening's events to Cinderella.

'The Prince had eyes for no one but the mysterious girl,' said one.

'Imagine her running out on him like that,' said the other.

'Of course, he raced after her,' said the first sister, 'but there was no sign of her — only a glass slipper which she had obviously lost in her haste.'

'He refused to dance with anyone after that,' the second sister sulked. 'And worse of all,' she gasped, 'rumour has it that he will only marry the girl whose foot will fit the slipper.'

At last Cinderella was allowed to go to bed only to dream of the handsome Prince and reflect on the wonderful evening she had spent with him.

The very next day Cinderella heard the King's heralds in the street. They were reading out a royal proclamation which said that every young lady in the city had to try on the glass slipper and that whoever it fitted would become the bride of the young Prince.

The two stepsisters fussed around Cinderella in the kitchen for the rest of the morning waiting for their chance to try on the slipper.

At last the long-awaited knock came on the front door and the sisters admitted the King's attendants. One was carrying the glass slipper on a red velvet cushion.

The first sister sat down on a chair and offered her bare foot. The attendant tried the slipper but it was too small.

'Your feet are much too big,' cried the second girl almost knocking her sister off the chair. 'Now it's my turn!' and she stuck out an ugly knobbly foot in front of the attendant.

The eager girl pushed and pressed, but no matter how hard she tried, she could get little more than her big toe into the dainty slipper.

'I'm afraid, Madam,' said the attendant politely to the red-faced girl, 'that this slipper is meant for a sleeker foot than yours.'

The two sisters begged to try the slipper on again but the attendant was firm. 'Is there no one else who could try on the slipper?' he asked when they had calmed down at last.

'No one,' they snapped in unison.

But a sharp-eyed attendant had spotted Cinderella hiding in a corner and he beckoned her to him.

'Every young girl has the right to try on the slipper,' he said to the sisters as they tried to push Cinderella out of the room.

'But she's only a servant girl,' said one.

'Not fitted to be the bride of a Prince,' said the other.

Nevertheless, Cinderella did try on the slipper and her two stepsisters gasped as they watched it slip easily on to her dainty foot.

The attendants clapped their hands with joy. 'It fits!' they cried.

When Cinderella produced the other slipper

from its hiding place it completely stunned her two stepsisters into silence.

Then something wonderful happened. Cinderella's fairy godmother appeared and with a wave of her wand, turned Cinderella's rags into another beautiful gown.

The stepsisters gasped: 'Why, it's the girl from the ball!'

Then without any more ado, Cinderella was whisked off to the palace where she fell into the arms of her handsome Prince.

Three days later Cinderella married her Prince. It was a grand affair and the Queen nudged the King at the wedding feast.

'What did I say? Wasn't I right?'

Indeed, the Queen was right. The Prince settled down with his lovely bride and ruled the country wisely and justly, and they lived in peace and happiness for the rest of their lives.